Facts That Last
Multiplication

**A Balanced Approach
to Memorization**

Larry Leutzinger

Creative Publications®

A Tribune Education Company

Acknowledgments

Contributing Writers Janet Pittock, Jeffrey Stiegel

Editor Diane Nieker

Creative Director Karen Lee

Design Gerta Sorensen

Cover Illustration Amanda Haley

Illustrators Sarah Frederking, Amanda Haley

Production Carlisle Communications, Ltd.

©1999 Creative Publications®, Inc.

Two Prudential Plaza, Suite 1175

Chicago, IL 60601

Creative Publications is a registered trademark.

Printed in the United States of America.

ISBN 0-7622-1213-6

Catalog No. 32312

Customer Service 800-624-0822

http://www.creativepublications.com

2 3 4 5 6 7 8 ML 05 04 03 02 01 00

Contents

Teacher Notes

Introduction	iv
Strategy Chart	v
Using this Book	vi
Prerequisites	viii

Zero, One, and Ten Rules

Overview	2
Warm-ups	4
The Easy Facts	6
Practice	10

Commutative Property

Overview	12
Warm-ups	14
Rows of Squares	20
Practice	22

Doubles and Five-0s

Overview	24
Warm-ups	26
Double Trouble	30
Nickels and Dimes	32
Practice	34

Patterns with Nines

Overview	38
Warm-ups	40
Patterns with Nines	42
Practice	46

Counting Threes

Overview	48
Warm-ups	50
Multiples of Three	54
Practice	58

Splitting Fours

Overview	62
Warm-ups	64
Four-Row Arrays	66
Practice	70

Ways with Sixes

Overview	72
Warm-ups	74
Six-Row Arrays	78
Practice	82

Resources

Multiplication Charts	86
Bibliography and About the Author	88

Introduction

The teaching of basic facts is an important component of any successful mathematics program. Many of the recommendations made by the National Council of Teachers of Mathematics (NCTM) in the *1989 Standards* assume students have fluency with basic facts. In its draft of *Standards 2000,* the NCTM clearly states that students need to memorize basic facts. Mastery of this information is necessary for developing both mental math and estimation skills. Many mathematical tasks become more efficient when basic facts can be recalled quickly and accurately.

In the past, the teaching of basic facts was often over-emphasized with too much time devoted to repetitive practice. The techniques presented in this book will help students remember their multiplication facts with a more appropriate amount of practice. The activities in *Facts That Last* provide the central portion of a successful three-step sequence for teaching basic fact mastery.

Acquiring an understanding of number relationships and the basic concepts of multiplication constitutes the first step in the process of mastering basic facts. (See prerequisites beginning on page viii.) The contents of this book address the second step—developing strategies to facilitate recall. Thirdly, students need to keep facts "fresh" with an appropriate amount of continuing practice. Practice can come from working on isolated facts or from working on facts embedded in activities that are more complex.

The approaches in this book demonstrate how facts can be organized into groups that can be handled with generalizations. With this knowledge, the effort of learning 121 multiplication facts is reduced to the ease of recognizing patterns and remembering a handful of rules. Mathematically powerful students often use such strategies naturally. When you encourage students in your class to examine and discuss the patterns and number relationships presented in this book, you make that power available to your entire class!

The seven approaches to learning multiplication facts that are included in this book are the zero, one, and ten rules; commutative property; doubles and five-0s; patterns with nines; counting threes; splitting fours; and ways with sixes. See the next page for a chart listing these strategies.

You may notice that four facts (7×7, 8×8, 7×8, and 8×7) are not covered by the strategies in this book. A study of square numbers will familiarize students with 7×7 and 8×8. Many students use the mnemonic $56 = 7 \times 8$, noticing that the numerals follow the order 5, 6, 7, 8, to help them remember the remaining two facts.

Strategy Chart

Zero, One, and Ten Rules

Zero multiplied by any number is zero. Any number multiplied by one is itself. To multiply by ten, first multiply by one, then add a zero to the ones place of the product.

Commutative Property

The same two factors always yield the same product, no matter what their order. $3 \times 8 = 24$ and $8 \times 3 = 24$.

Doubles and Five-0s

Multiplying by two is the same as adding doubles in addition. For example, $6 \times 2 = 6 + 6 = 12$. Multiplying any number by five yields a product with either five or zero in the ones place. Multiples of five include 5, 10, 15, 20, . . .

Patterns with Nines

When nine is a factor, the digits of the product always add to nine. $7 \times 9 = 63$ and $6 + 3 = 9$.

Counting Threes

Counting by threes can be used to find multiples of three.

Splitting Fours

When multiplying by four, split four into two twos and double the twos fact. $8 \times 4 =$ the double of $8 \times 2 = 16 + 16 = 32$.

Ways with Sixes

To multiply by six, double the threes fact. $4 \times 6 =$ the double of $4 \times 3 = 12 + 12 = 24$. Or, think five groups of the number plus one more group. $6 \times 7 = 5 \times 7 + 7$.

How This Book Is Organized

How to Use This Book

Facts That Last combines lessons that present strategies and practice to help students memorize their facts. You may choose to supplement or replace the work in your mathematics textbook with this material. You may choose to use the entire book, or just the strategies your students need most.

Teaching Sequence

First, determine that your students are ready to memorize. The prerequisites chart (pages viii–1) lists evidences of readiness. Should you determine that students are not ready, you will find suggested activities and resources listed in the prerequisite chart.

At the beginning of each strategy section you'll find an overview that provides a summary of the technique, prerequisites specific to that approach, information about when to use the technique, and additional strategy-related experiences for your students. You'll also find references to the optional practice book.

Each fact-group section starts with warm-ups. Warm-ups include introductory experiences, mental math experiences, and a refreshing of the skills students need to work with the fact group. These warm-ups are designed to take approximately three to five minutes. Some sections have five warm-ups while others have ten. Many teachers enjoy using these warm-ups during the transition time between activities or when students are lining up.

Next comes an activity that takes at least one class period. The activities are designed to give students experience and practice with the strategy. Activities may be done as a whole class, in cooperative groups, or individually.

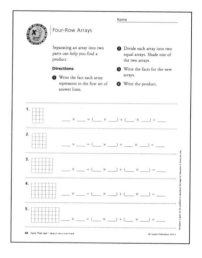

The third component of each section is practice. Practice is similar in format and feel to the warm-ups. The practices focus on using the strategy to recall facts quickly and correctly.

Once the students in your class have memorized their multiplication facts, you can help them maintain quick and accurate recall by providing engaging ways to practice those facts. See the bibliography (page 88) for more complete information about suggested resources.

Talk About It

Students who talk about their own thinking and hear how other students think are more likely to use helpful techniques. You'll find hints for leading discourse about students' thinking throughout the book. Often, questions for leading a class discussion will appear at the beginning of a set of warm-ups or practice pages. These questions should be used throughout the warm-up or practice period. You'll also find questions that ask students to describe their thinking embedded in the activities.

Materials

Teacher notes found at the beginning of activities, warm-ups, and practice sets tell you what supplies are needed for the activity. The items listed, however, are by no means the only materials that can be used. If you don't have the specific equipment named, use alternative materials that are available to you. Materials lists for some of the activities offer suggestions for alternatives.

The following materials are suggested for use with activities in this book.

▶ 20 LinkerCubes® for each student

▶ Play money, ten (10) dimes and five (5) nickels for each student

▶ Base ten blocks

▶ Hundred chart

Prerequisites

Research has shown that students with a solid conceptual foundation are more successful memorizing their facts. The following chart summarizes key concepts your students should fully understand before they are asked to memorize. If your students own the concepts listed in the first column of the chart, they are ready to begin successfully committing their facts to memory. However, if you determine that your students need more experiences before they begin the activities in this book, you might start with the suggestions offered in the second column of the chart. Additional activities can be found in the resources listed in the third column. A bibliography is located on page 88.

Key Concepts

Students can explain that multiplication is combining groups of equal numbers of items. They can model multiplication situations with cubes or other manipulatives.

Students use multiplication facts correctly to describe the rows and columns of an array of items.

Students have methods to figure out the correct answers to multiplication facts. These may include counting on fingers, using manipulatives, relating the problem to another fact that is similar, and using number sense to find the unknown answer.

Students demonstrate how to use repeated addition to find unknown products.

Students understand relationships of numbers from 0 to 100. They demonstrate understanding of the base ten place-value system by identifying values of digits in different place value positions.

Students have an intuitive understanding of the commutative property of multiplication. They can match facts having the same factors in a different order and supply products without working through both exercises. For example, they find $4 \times 9 = 36$, and they can immediately tell the answer for the related fact ($9 \times 4 = 36$).

If Your Students Need More Experiences	Recommended Resources
Use margarine tubs and LinkerCubes® to model multiplication. Place the same number of cubes in each tub, and then describe the set of tubs with a multiplication fact. 	*Constructing Ideas About Multiplication and Division* by Julie Pier Brodie. *Understanding Multiplication & Division* by Linda Holden and Micaelia Randolph Brummett.
Use counters to make arrays. Describe the arrays as the number of rows times the number of counters in each row. Write the multiplication fact that represents the array. 	*Constructing Ideas About Multiplication and Division* by Julie Pier Brodie. *Understanding Multiplication & Division* by Linda Holden and Micaelia Randolph Brummett.
Give students opportunities to work with situations that include multiplication. Provide opportunities for students to discuss how they solve multiplication facts they do not have memorized.	*Smart Arithmetic: A Thinking Approach to Computation, Grades 4–6* by Rhea Irvine and Kathryn Walker.
Have students use a hundred chart to mark multiples by adding on. 	*Understanding Multiplication & Division* by Linda Holden and Micaelia Randolph Brummett.
Use base ten blocks to model numbers from 0 to 100. Model many ways numbers can be shown. For example, 24 could be 2 ten rods and 4 units, or 1 ten rod and 14 units, or 24 units.	*Ready to Go! with Base Ten Blocks* by Ann Roper and Charlene Margot.
Have students draw an array of dots such as 2 rows of 4 dots. Ask students to describe the array with a multiplication fact (2 × 4 = 8), then turn the array 90° and describe the array with the related fact (4 × 2 = 8). 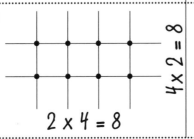	*Understanding Multiplication & Division* by Linda Holden and Micaelia Randolph Brummett.

Zero, One, and Ten Rules Overview

What Are the Zero, One, and Ten Rules?

With the zero, one, and ten rules, students focus on consistent multiplication patterns that are easy to observe and simple to describe. The rules that describe multiplying with zero, one, and ten are:

▶ **Zero** Any number multiplied by zero is zero.

▶ **One** Any number multiplied by one is the number itself.

▶ **Ten** Any number multiplied by ten is the same number with a zero added to the ones place.

When to Use the Zero, One, and Ten Rules

These rules work for multiplication facts that have factors of 0, 1, or 10.

×	0	1	2	3	4	5	6	7	8	9	10
0	0	0	0	0	0	0	0	0	0	0	0
1	0	1	2	3	4	5	6	7	8	9	10
2	0	2									20
3	0	3									30
4	0	4									40
5	0	5									50
6	0	6									60
7	0	7									70
8	0	8									80
9	0	9									90
10	0	10	20	30	40	50	60	70	80	90	100

Prerequisites

Students should understand multiplication concepts (pages viii-1) and should be able to identify and describe patterns.

Additional Experiences

Distribute base ten blocks. Instruct students to make displays of the equal groups you describe. Have students relate a multiplication fact to each display. Present facts such as these:

▶ **Using zero as a factor**

5 groups of 0 (5 × 0 = 0)

0 groups of 8 (0 × 8 = 0)

▶ **Using one as a factor**

3 groups of 1 (3 × 1 = 3)

1 group of 6 (1 × 6 = 6)

▶ **Using ten as a factor**

Model facts with base ten rods.

6 groups of 10 (six ten rods, 6 × 10, or 60)

4 groups of 10 (four tens rods, 4 × 10, or 40)

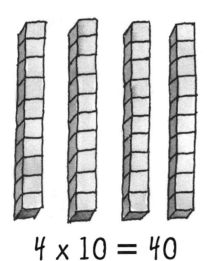

4 x 10 = 40

You can find additional practice in *Practice Your Facts, Levels 1–5,* by Creative Publications, Inc.

Zero, One, and Ten Rules

Warm-ups

Each warm-up exercise set should take two (2) or three (3) minutes. The short problem sets are great for filling transition times. Some teachers use them while students stand in line.

Talk About It

As you work through these warm-ups, ask students to talk about their thinking. This not only helps you assess, but gives students a chance to clarify their thinking and to hear about ways of thinking that might be different from theirs. You might ask questions like

If there are 0 things in each group, how many things will there be altogether? (0)

If there is 1 item in each group, how many items will there be altogether? (The number will be the same as the number of groups)

If there are 10 articles in each group, how many articles will there be altogether? (The number of groups times ten)

....

Day 1

Pose these questions.

Suppose there are 4 children, each with 0 ice cream cones. How many ice cream cones altogether?
(0 ice cream cones)

Suppose you have 9 groups of 0. How many altogether?
(0)

Continue this activity with 1–10 groups of 0.

....

Day 2

Pose these questions.

Suppose there are 9 children, each with 1 balloon. How many balloons altogether?
(9 balloons)

Suppose you have 3 coin purses, each with 1 coin. How many coins altogether?
(3 coins)

Continue to present situations of 1–10 groups with 1 item in each group, asking

How many altogether?

Day 3

Pose these questions.

Suppose there are 2 children with 10 dimes each. How many dimes altogether?
(20 dimes)

Suppose you have 7 dishes with 10 crackers on each. How many crackers altogether?
(70 crackers)

Continue to present situations of 1–10 groups with 10 items in each group, asking

How many altogether?

Day 4

Show a number card such as 5.

Add 0 this many times. How many altogether?
(0)

Add 1 this many times. How many altogether?
(5)

Add 10 this many times. How many altogether?
(50)

Continue to show number cards 1–10 to represent the number of times students should add 1, 0, or 10 together.

Day 5

Show a number card such as 9.

Add 0 this many times. How many altogether?
(0)

Add 1 this many times. How many altogether?
(9)

Add 10 this many times. How many altogether?
(90)

Continue to show number cards 1–10 to represent the number of times students should add 1, 0, or 10 together.

The Easy Facts

Summary

Students use dimes to explore multiplying-10 and discuss patterns they find that will help make these facts easy to remember. Students also identify patterns that occur when multiplying with 0 or 1 as a factor.

Whole Class Activity

Materials

Ten (10) play money dimes for each student

Directions

❶ Ask students to display three (3) dimes.

   What is the value of 3 dimes? (30 cents)

   What multiplication fact would three dimes represent? ($3 \times 10 = 30$)

❷ Try several similar activities, recording each multiplying-10 fact on the board.

❸ With your class, write the multiplying-10 facts in order from $1 \times 10 = 10$ through $10 \times 10 = 100$.

❹ Have students explore patterns for multiplying-0 and facts for multiplying-1 by repeating these activities with each of those sets of facts.

$$1 \times 10 = 10$$
$$2 \times 10 = 20$$
$$3 \times 10 = 30$$
$$4 \times 10 = 40$$
$$5 \times 10 = 50$$
$$6 \times 10 = 60$$
$$7 \times 10 = 70$$
$$8 \times 10 = 80$$
$$9 \times 10 = 90$$
$$10 \times 10 = 100$$

Talk About It

What patterns do you notice for the multiplication facts that have 10 as a factor? (Accept any reasonable answers.)

Who can give a rule to follow for finding products that have a factor of 10? (Rules should reflect understanding that the number gains an additional digit, and that digit is a zero in the ones place.)

Extension or Homework

Provide a copy of Fact Race 1, page 8, for each student. Have students complete the page of facts as quickly and accurately as they can. At the end of each ten-second period, make a tally mark on the board. When students complete their facts, have them record the number of tally marks that appear on the board onto their papers. Repeat this procedure with Fact Race 2, page 9.

You might want to use Fact Race 2 after completing the practice section of zeros, ones, and tens to see how students have improved.

note Before handing out Fact Race, offer hints about completing timed tasks. Instruct students to skip facts they have to think about. When they finish completing those facts they know immediately, students can go back and complete those facts they need to think about.

Fact Race 1

Complete these facts as quickly as you can!

$0 \times 6 =$ _____ $10 \times 9 =$ _____

$5 \times 1 =$ _____ $0 \times 7 =$ _____

$9 \times 0 =$ _____ $1 \times 0 =$ _____

$1 \times 2 =$ _____ $10 \times 3 =$ _____

$0 \times 0 =$ _____ $1 \times 6 =$ _____

$1 \times 5 =$ _____ $5 \times 10 =$ _____

$0 \times 2 =$ _____ $0 \times 10 =$ _____

$0 \times 3 =$ _____ $1 \times 9 =$ _____

$10 \times 4 =$ _____ $4 \times 0 =$ _____

$1 \times 8 =$ _____ $8 \times 10 =$ _____

$10 \times 8 =$ _____ $7 \times 0 =$ _____

$1 \times 10 =$ _____ $3 \times 10 =$ _____

$0 \times 5 =$ _____ $1 \times 3 =$ _____

$6 \times 10 =$ _____ $9 \times 1 =$ _____

$0 \times 9 =$ _____ $5 \times 0 =$ _____

Finish _____

Fact Race 2

Complete these facts as quickly as you can!

0 × 8	10 × 5	7 × 10	0 × 4	3 × 1
10 × 10	0 × 1	10 × 0	10 × 9	2 × 1
1 × 7	10 × 6	8 × 1	0 × 4	6 × 1
10 × 7	4 × 10	4 × 1	6 × 0	10 × 2
8 × 0	10 × 0	10 × 3	10 × 9	1 × 7
2 × 0	7 × 1	3 × 0	2 × 10	10 × 1

Finish_____

Zero, One, and Ten Rules

Practice

Work on these sets of practice exercises until students get each answer within three (3) seconds. Ask students to state the entire fact rather than just the answer ("2 × 0 = 0" instead of "0"). Stating the complete fact improves students' recall. Present the facts in various ways. Ask the students to listen and then reply verbally, or use flash cards and have the students write their facts. Varying the format helps all students focus on the facts.

Talk About It

Ask students questions like

How do you remember facts with 0 as a factor?
(Any number multiplied by zero is zero.)

How do you remember facts with 1 as a factor?
(Any number multiplied by one is itself.)

How do you remember facts with 10 as a factor?
(The number moves one place to the left and you put a zero in the ones place.)

Day 1

Present these facts.

0 × 6 (0)	1 × 3 (3)
0 × 5 (0)	0 × 9 (0)
8 × 10 (80)	0 × 0 (0)
5 × 1 (5)	0 × 7 (0)
6 × 10 (60)	9 × 1 (9)
7 × 0 (0)	1 × 5 (5)
9 × 0 (0)	1 × 1 (1)
3 × 10 (30)	5 × 0 (0)
1 × 2 (2)	9 × 10 (90)
10 × 9 (90)	10 × 3 (30)

Extension Present facts in which any number is multiplied by 0 (or 0 is multiplied by any number).

Day 2

Present these facts.

0 × 8 (0)	10 × 8 (80)
0 × 3 (0)	1 × 9 (9)
1 × 6 (6)	3 × 1 (3)
10 × 5 (50)	1 × 10 (10)
10 × 4 (40)	4 × 0 (0)
5 × 10 (50)	2 × 0 (0)
7 × 10 (70)	10 × 10 (100)
1 × 8 (8)	4 × 1 (4)
0 × 10 (0)	0 × 1 (0)
0 × 5 (0)	6 × 0 (0)

Extension Present facts in which any number is multiplied by 1 (or 1 is multiplied by any number).

Day 3

Present these facts.

10 × 9 (90)	0 × 4 (0)
10 × 2 (20)	10 × 1 (10)
0 × 6 (0)	6 × 1 (6)
7 × 1 (7)	1 × 2 (2)
2 × 10 (20)	10 × 7 (70)
8 × 0 (0)	4 × 10 (40)
10 × 6 (60)	8 × 10 (80)
10 × 0 (0)	7 × 0 (0)
8 × 1 (8)	3 × 10 (30)
5 × 1 (5)	1 × 3 (3)

Extension Present facts in which a number 1–10 is multiplied by 10 (or 10 is multiplied by a number 1–10).

Day 4

Present these facts.

4 × 10 (40)	1 × 4 (4)
2 × 0 (0)	1 × 8 (8)
0 × 9 (0)	6 × 1 (6)
1 × 10 (10)	7 × 10 (70)
10 × 7 (70)	5 × 10 (50)
3 × 1 (3)	10 × 4 (40)
1 × 9 (9)	10 × 1 (10)
10 × 8 (80)	0 × 4 (0)
3 × 0 (0)	10 × 5 (50)
0 × 4 (0)	1 × 6 (6)

Extension Present facts in which a number 1–20 is multiplied by 10 (or 10 is multiplied by a number 1–20).

Day 5

Present these facts.

0 × 9 (0)	1 × 5 (5)
5 × 1 (5)	9 × 0 (0)
8 × 1 (8)	2 × 10 (20)
0 × 8 (0)	9 × 1 (9)
10 × 3 (30)	0 × 7 (0)
0 × 2 (0)	1 × 1 (1)
10 × 0 (0)	7 × 1 (7)
10 × 6 (60)	6 × 10 (60)
5 × 0 (0)	1 × 3 (3)
1 × 0 (0)	10 × 9 (90)

Extension Present facts in which any number is multiplied by 0, 1, or 10 (or 0, 1, or 10 are multiplied by any number).

Commutative Property Overview

What is the Commutative Property?

The commutative property of multiplication is the mathematical rule that states that the order of the factors has no effect on the product. Therefore, $3 \times 7 = 7 \times 3$. Knowledge of the commutative property helps students cut the number of facts to be memorized nearly in half.

When to Use the Commutative Property

The commutative property can be used for all multiplication facts. When a student learns a multiplication fact, the product for a second fact that has the same factors in reverse order can easily be recalled by applying the commutative property.

×	0	1	2	3	4	5	6	7	8	9	10
0	0	0	0	0	0	0	0	0	0	0	0
1	0	1	2	3	4	5	6	7	8	9	10
2	0	2	4	6	8	10	12	14	16	18	20
3	0	3	6	9	12	18	15	21	24	28	30
4	0	4	8	12	16	20	24	28	32	36	40
5	0	5	10	15	20	25	30	35	40	45	50
6	0	6	12	18	24	30	36	42	48	54	60
7	0	7	14	21	28	35	42	49	56	63	70
8	0	8	16	24	32	40	48	56	64	72	80
9	0	9	18	27	36	45	54	63	72	81	90
10	0	10	20	30	40	50	60	70	80	90	100

Prerequisites

Students should understand multiplication concepts and have an intuitive understanding of the commutative property of multiplication (pages vi-vii).

Additional Experiences

Have students work in pairs to build rectangular prisms with LinkerCubes®. Students should first describe each prism they make with a multiplication fact (the number of rows times the number of cubes in each row), then turn their rectangle 90° and describe it with another multiplication fact (the number of rows times the number of cubes in each row). Provide an opportunity for students to report their results and record the pairs of facts found. Ask students to look for and describe patterns.

You can find additional practice in *Practice Your Facts, Levels 1–5,* by Creative Publications, Inc.

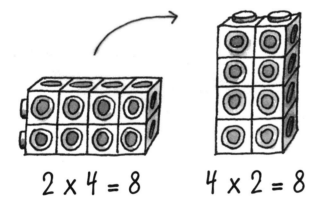

$$2 \times 4 = 8 \qquad 4 \times 2 = 8$$

Commutative Property

Warm-ups

Each warm-up exercise set should take two (2) or three (3) minutes. The short sets of exercises are great for filling transition times. Some teachers use them while students stand in line.

Talk About It

As you work through these warm-ups, ask students to talk about their thinking. This not only helps you assess, but gives students a chance to clarify their thinking and to hear about ways of thinking that might be different from theirs. You might ask questions like

What is multiplication? (A shortcut for repeatedly adding the same number.)

What is the commutative property of multiplication? (Changing the order of the factors does not change the product.)

What other operation is commutative? (Addition)

Day 1

Pose these questions. Record facts on chalkboard or overhead.

Picture 3 children, each child holding 2 balloons.

What fact multiplication describes this picture? (3 × 2) Record the fact.

How many balloons altogether? (6 balloons)

Picture 2 children, each child holding 3 balloons.

What multiplication fact describes this picture? (2 × 3) Record the fact.

How many balloons altogether? (6 balloons)

What do you notice about this pair of facts? (The factors are the same, but in reverse order, and the product is the same.)

Picture 5 book bags, each with 1 book. How many books altogether? (5 books)

What multiplication fact describes this picture? (5 × 1 = 5) Record the fact.

Picture 1 book bag with 5 books.

What multiplication fact describes this picture? (1 × 5) Record the fact.

How many books altogether? (5 books)

What do you notice about this pair of facts? (The factors are the same, but in reverse order, and the product is the same.)

Continue to present situations with 1–5 groups, each with 1–5 items.

Day 2

Pose these questions. Record facts on chalk-board or overhead.

Picture 4 cars, each with 5 passengers.

What fact multiplication describes this picture?
(4 × 5) Record the fact.

How many passengers altogether?
(20 passengers)

Picture 5 cars, each with 4 passengers.

What multiplication fact describes this picture?
(5 × 4) Record the fact.

How many passengers altogether?
(20 passengers)

What do you notice about this pair of facts?
(The factors are the same, but in reverse order, and the product is the same.)

Picture 5 crayon boxes, each with 3 crayons.

What multiplication fact describes this picture?
(5 × 3)

How many crayons altogether? (15 crayons)
Record the fact.

Picture 3 crayon boxes, each with 5 crayons.

What multiplication fact describes this picture?
(3 × 5) Record the fact.

How many crayons altogether? (15 crayons)

What do you notice about this pair of facts?
(The factors are the same, but in reverse order, and the product is the same.)

Continue to present situations with 1–5 groups, each with 1–5 items.

Day 3

Pose these questions. Record facts on chalk-board or overhead.

Picture 2 bowls, each with 4 pieces of fruit.

What fact multiplication describes this picture?
(2 × 4) Record the fact.

How many pieces of fruit altogether?
(8 pieces of fruit)

Picture 4 bowls, each with two pieces of fruit.

What multiplication fact describes this picture?
(4 × 2) Record the fact.

How many pieces of fruit altogether?
(8 pieces of fruit)

What do you notice about this pair of facts?
(The factors are the same, but in reverse order, and the product is the same.)

Picture 2 shirts, each with 5 buttons.

What multiplication fact describes this picture?
(2 × 5) Record the fact.

How many buttons altogether? (10 buttons)

Picture 5 shirts, each with 2 buttons.

What multiplication fact describes this picture?
(5 × 2) Record the fact.

How many buttons altogether? (10 buttons)

What do you notice about this pair of facts?
(The factors are the same, but in reverse order, and the product is the same.)

Continue to present situations with 1–5 or 10 groups, each with 1–5 or 10 items.

Day 4

Write a number sentence on chalkboard or overhead, then pose questions.

3 × 4 = 12

Can you give another multiplication sentence using 3, 4, and 12? (4 × 3 = 12) Record.

8 × 4 = 32

Can you give another multiplication fact using 8, 4, and 32? (4 × 8 = 32) Record.

Continue to present a sentence, write it on the board, then ask for a related sentence using the same numbers and write it.

Day 5

Ask students for related multiplication sentences. Record sentences on chalkboard or overhead.

Give the related multiplication sentence for 2 × 5 = 10. The sentence must use the same factors, but in different order.
(5 × 2 = 10)

Give the related multiplication sentence for 7 × 5 = 35. The sentence must use the same factors, but in different order.
(5 × 7 = 35)

Continue this activity pairing numbers 0–10.

Day 6

Ask students for related multiplication sentences. Record facts on chalkboard or overhead.

Give the related multiplication sentence for 2 × 9 = 18. The sentence must contain the 2, 9, and 18. (9 × 2 = 18)

Give the related multiplication sentence for 5 × 6 = 30. The sentence must contain 5, 6, and 30. (6 × 5 = 30)

Continue this activity pairing a number 0–5 with a number 1–10.

Day 7

Ask students for related multiplication sentence. Record facts on chalkboard or overhead.

Give the related multiplication sentence for 1 × 9 = 9. (9 × 1 = 9)

Give the related multiplication sentence for 4 × 8 = 32. (8 × 4 = 32)

Continue this activity pairing a number 0–5 with a number 1–10.

Day 8

Ask students for related multiplication facts. Record facts on chalkboard or overhead.

Give a complete multiplication fact with the numbers 2 and 7 as factors. ($2 \times 7 = 14$ or $7 \times 2 = 14$)

Give the complete related fact. ($7 \times 2 = 14$ or $2 \times 7 = 14$)

Give a complete multiplication fact with the numbers 5 and 3 as factors. ($5 \times 3 = 15$ or $3 \times 5 = 15$)

Give the complete related fact. ($3 \times 5 = 15$ or $5 \times 3 = 15$)

Continue this activity pairing a number 0–5 with a number 1–10.

Day 9

Ask students for related multiplication facts.

Give a complete multiplication fact with the numbers 1 and 6 as factors. ($1 \times 6 = 6$ or $6 \times 1 = 6$)

Give the complete related multiplication fact. ($6 \times 1 = 6$ or $1 \times 6 = 6$)

Give a complete multiplication fact with the numbers 5 and 10 as factors. ($5 \times 10 = 50$ or $10 \times 5 = 50$)

Give the complete related multiplication fact. ($9 \times 5 = 45$ or $5 \times 9 = 45$)

Continue this activity pairing a number 1–5 with a number 0–10.

Day 10

Ask students for related multiplication facts.

Give a complete multiplication fact with the numbers 3 and 6 as factors. ($3 \times 6 = 18$ or $6 \times 3 = 18$)

Give a complete related multiplication fact. ($6 \times 3 = 18$ or $3 \times 6 = 18$)

Give a complete multiplication fact with the numbers 5 and 9 as factors. ($5 \times 9 = 45$ and $9 \times 5 = 45$)

Give a complete related multiplication fact. ($9 \times 5 = 45$ and $5 \times 9 = 45$)

Continue this activity pairing a number 0–5 with a number 0–10.

Rows of Squares

Summary

Students use grid paper to make rectangles, then describe their rectangles with two related multiplication facts.

Individual Activity

Materials

Each student needs

▶ One (1) copy of Rows of Squares, page 20

▶ Two (2) or three (3) copies of Grid Paper, page 21

▶ Scissors, blank paper, and glue

Getting Ready

Prepare a 3 × 5 grid-paper rectangle large enough to be seen by all students. You may wish to use an overhead transparency.

---

note Some students may create squares with the grid paper. In such cases, they will find only one multiplication fact to describe the square because the number in each row is the same as the number of rows.

Directions

❶ Show students the prepared 3 × 5 rectangle. Position it so that it has 3 rows with 5 squares in each row.

How many rows does this rectangle have?
(3)

How many squares are in each row?
(5)

How many squares in all?
(15)

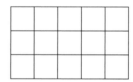

❷ Write *3 × 5 = 15* on the board.

This sentence describes the rectangle with three rows of five squares.

❸ Rotate the 3 × 5 rectangle 90°.

What multiplication sentence would we write for this rectangle?
(5 × 3 = 15) Remind students what each number in the sentence represents.

❹ Have students complete Rows of Squares, page 10, by creating their own rectangles on grid paper, then cutting the rectangles out and pasting them onto a piece of paper. Instruct students to write two multiplication sentences that describe each rectangle and place them appropriately on the side of and below the rectangle.

Talk About It

Ask students to share their rectangles and multiplication sentences. Record the pairs of sentences on the board. After several students have shared their rectangles and sentences, ask

Did you notice a pattern about the sentences that describe the rectangles? (The factors change positions but the products are the same. Accept all accurate responses.)

The sentence for a rectangle and the sentence for that same rectangle rotated 90° contain the same factors in reverse order. This is an example of the commutative property of multiplication—the order of the factors in a multiplication fact does not affect the product.

Extension or Homework

Show students how to make "cross-line arrays." Start with horizontal lines for the rows, then cross those lines with vertical lines for the number in each row. Draw a dot on each intersection of lines—the dots create the array.

Have students draw cross-line arrays to represent pairs of related facts and products.

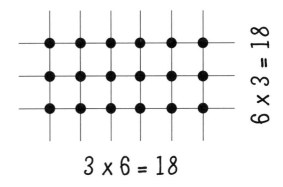

$$3 \times 6 = 18$$

$$6 \times 3 = 18$$

Rows of Squares

Make rectangles and then describe them two ways.

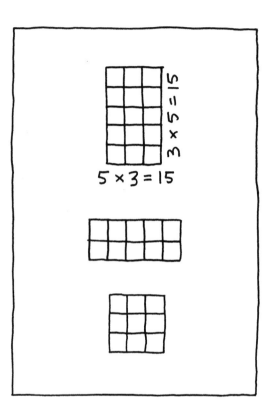

Directions

❶ Shade a rectangle on the grid paper. Then cut the rectangle from the grid paper.

❷ Paste the rectangle on a blank piece of paper.

❸ Write a multiplication fact below the rectangle that describes the number of rows and the number of squares in each row. Include the product.

❹ Turn the paper 90° to the right and write the fact that describes the rectangle in that position. Include the product.

❺ Make as many rectangles and pairs of facts with their products to describe them as you can.

Commutative Property

Practice

Work on these sets of practice exercises until students get each answer within three (3) seconds. Ask students to state the entire fact rather than just the answer ("$2 \times 3 = 6$" instead of "2×3"). Stating the complete fact improves students' recall. Present the facts in various ways. Ask the students to listen and then reply verbally, or use flash cards and have the students write their facts. Varying the format helps all students focus on the facts.

Talk About It

Ask students to talk about their thinking. Follow up by asking if anyone has a different way to find the answer.

If $15 \times 5 = 75$, what is 5×15? (75)

How do you know? (Accept all accurate responses.)

Describe the commutative property of multiplication. (Any order of the same factors results in the same product. $x \times y = z$ and $y \times x = z$.)

Draw a picture or use manipulatives to demonstrate that changing the order of factors still produces the same product. (An example might be three vases, each with two flowers ($3 \times 2 = 6$), and two vases, each with three flowers ($3 \times 2 = 6$)).

....

Day 1

Have students make cross-line arrays by drawing horizontal and vertical lines as indicated.

Draw two horizontal lines. Next, draw four vertical lines.

What are two multiplication facts, with their products, that describe this array?
($2 \times 4 = 8$ and $4 \times 2 = 8$)

Draw four horizontal lines. Next, draw three vertical lines.

What are two multiplication facts, with their products, that describe this array?
($4 \times 3 = 12$ and $3 \times 4 = 12$)
Continue this activity having students draw arrays with either two or four horizontal lines and one to ten vertical lines.

Extension Have students draw arrays with either two or four horizontal lines and zero, eleven, or twelve vertical lines.

....

Day 2

Follow directions for Day 1.

Draw three horizontal lines. Next, draw seven vertical lines.

What are two multiplication facts, with their products, tha describe this array?
($3 \times 7 = 21$ and $7 \times 3 = 21$)
Continue this activity having students draw arrays with either three or six horizontal lines and one to ten vertical lines.

Extension Have students draw arrays with either three or six horizontal lines and zero, eleven, or twelve vertical lines.

Day 3

Follow directions for Day 1.

Draw five vertical lines. Next, draw two horizontal lines.

What are two multiplication facts, with their products, that describe this array?
$(2 \times 5 = 10$ or $5 \times 2 = 10)$

Draw ten vertical lines. Next, draw four horizontal lines.

What are two multiplication facts, with their products, that describe this array?
$(4 \times 10 = 40$ and $10 \times 4 = 40)$

Continue this activity having students draw arrays with either five or ten vertical lines and one to ten horizontal lines.

Day 4

Ask students to give another complete fact that is sure to have the same product because it has the same factors. Pause before giving the product to encourage students to think of the answer on their own.

$2 \times 6 = 12 \ (6 \times 2 = 12)$
$1 \times 8 = 8 \ (8 \times 1 = 8)$
$0 \times 5 = 0 \ (5 \times 0 = 0)$
$3 \times 9 = 27 \ (9 \times 3 = 27)$
$2 \times 7 = 14 \ (7 \times 2 = 14)$
$3 \times 10 = 30 \ (10 \times 3 = 30)$
$3 \times 5 = 15 \ (5 \times 3 = 15)$
$2 \times 9 = 18 \ (9 \times 2 = 18)$
$3 \times 7 = 21 \ (7 \times 3 = 21)$

Extension Present facts that have a factor of 11 or 12.

Day 5

Follow directions for Day 4.

$6 \times 3 = 18 \ (3 \times 6 = 18)$
$3 \times 4 = 12 \ (4 \times 3 = 12)$
$10 \times 2 = 20 \ (2 \times 10 = 20)$
$0 \times 6 = 0 \ (6 \times 0 = 0)$
$3 \times 0 = 0 \ (0 \times 3 = 0)$
$5 \times 4 = 20 \ (4 \times 5 = 20)$
$4 \times 8 = 32 \ (8 \times 4 = 32)$
$3 \times 8 = 24 \ (8 \times 3 = 24)$
$10 \times 4 = 40 \ (4 \times 10 = 40)$

Extension Present facts that have a factor of 11 or 12.

Doubles and Five-0s Overview

What are the Doubles and Five-0s Strategies?

With doubles and five-0s, students focus on the multiplication tables of 2 and 5. These facts have easy-to-observe patterns that are simple for students to find and describe.

These rules apply:

▶ **Doubles** Multiplying by two is the same as adding the number to itself or the doubles facts for addition. In either case the number is doubled. For example, 4×2 is the equal to $4 + 4$, or 8.

▶ **Five-0s** The product of any number and five will have either a five or a zero in the ones place.

When to Use Doubles and Five-0s

These patterns occur with multiplication facts that have a factor of two or five.

×	0	1	2	3	4	5	6	7	8	9	10
0			0			0					
1			2			5					
2	0	2	4	6	8	10	12	14	16	18	20
3			6			15					
4			8			20					
5	0	5	10	15	20	25	30	35	40	45	50
6			12			30					
7			14			35					
8			16			40					
9			18			45					
10			20			50					

Prerequisites

Students should understand multiplication concepts (pages viii-1). They should know their doubles facts for addition.

Additional Experiences

Have students shade multiples of two on a hundred chart. Ask students to describe the patterns they find. Using a fresh hundred chart, repeat this activity for multiples of five.

You can find additional practice in *Practice Your Facts, Levels 1–5*, by Creative Publications, Inc.

1	2	3	4	5	6	7	8	9	10
11	12	13	14	15	16	17	18	19	20
21	22	23	24	25	26	27	28	29	30
31	32	33	34	35	36	37	38	39	40
41	42	43	44	45	46	47	48	49	50
51	52	53	54	55	56	57	58	59	60
61	62	63	64	65	66	67	68	69	70
71	72	73	74	75	76	77	78	79	80
81	82	83	84	85	86	87	88	89	90
91	92	93	94	95	96	97	98	99	100

1	2	3	4	5	6	7	8	9	10
11	12	13	14	15	16	17	18	19	20
21	22	23	24	25	26	27	28	29	30
31	32	33	34	35	36	37	38	39	40
41	42	43	44	45	46	47	48	49	50
51	52	53	54	55	56	57	58	59	60
61	62	63	64	65	66	67	68	69	70
71	72	73	74	75	76	77	78	79	80
81	82	83	84	85	86	87	88	89	90
91	92	93	94	95	96	97	98	99	100

Doubles and Five-0s

Warm-ups

Each warm-up exercise set should take two (2) or three (3) minutes. The short sets of exercises are great for filling transition times. Some teachers use them while students stand in line.

Talk About It

As you work through these warm-ups, ask students to talk about their thinking. This not only helps you assess, but gives students a chance to clarify their thinking and to hear about ways of thinking that might be different from theirs. You might ask questions like

Can you think of an addition fact using two numbers that will give the same result as multiplying one of the numbers by 2? (Any doubles fact—the number plus itself)

What are the ones digits in multiples of 5? (5 or 0)

Day 1

Ask students to count as directed.

Start with 2. Count by 2 to 20.
(2, 4, 6, 8, 10, 12, 14, 16, 18, 20)

Start with 5. Count by 5 to 50.
(5, 10, 15, 20, 25, 30, 35, 40, 45, 50)

Repeat until most students can count quickly and accurately.

Day 2

Show the number card 7.

Count by 2. Start with 2 and count this many times.
(2, 4, 6, 8, 10, 12, 14)

What are seven 2s?
(14)

Count by 5. Start with 5 and count this many times.
(5, 10, 15, 20, 25, 30, 35)

What are seven 5s?
(35)

Show any number card 1–10 to represent the number of times students should count by either 2 or 5.

Day 3

Show the number card 4.

Count by 2. Start with 2 and count this many times.
(2, 4, 6, 8)

What are four 2s?
(8)

Count by 5. Start with 5 and count this many times.
(5, 10, 15, 20)

What are four 5s?
(20)

Show a number card 1–10 to represent the number of times students should count by either 2 or 5.

Day 4

Ask students to count as directed.

Count by 3. Start with three and count twice.
(3, 6)

What are two 3s?
(6)

Count by 3. Start with three and count 5 times.
(3, 6, 9, 12, 15)

What are five 3s?
(15)

Continue to have students count by a number 1–10 either 2 or 5 times.

Day 5

Ask students to count as directed.

Count by 2. Start with two and count 8 times.
(2, 4, 6, 8, 10, 12, 14, 16)

What are eight 2s?
(16)

Count by 5. Start with 5 and count 3 times.
(5, 10, 15)

What are three 5s?
(15)

Continue to have students count by 2 or by 5. Instruct students to count 1–10 times.

Day 6

Present these exercises.

What is the sum when two 8s are added together?
(16)

What is the sum when five 8s are added together?
(40)

What is the sum when two 4s are added together?
(8)

What is the sum when five 4s are added together?
(20)

Continue to ask students use a number 1–10 as an addend either 2 or 5 times.

Day 7

Pose these questions.

Suppose there are 2 books in each of 6 groups. How many books altogether?
(12 books)

Suppose there are 5 pencils in each of 4 groups. How many pencils altogether?
(20 pencils)

Continue to present situations of 1–10 groups, each with 2 or 5 items, asking

How many altogether?

Day 8

Pose these questions.

Suppose there are 2 children in each of 9 groups. How many children altogether?
(18 children)

Suppose there are 5 apples in each of 9 groups. How many apples altogether?
(45 apples)

Continue to present situations of 1–10 groups, each with 2 or 5 items, asking

How many altogether?

Day 9

Show a number card such as 5.

Suppose there are this number in each of 5 groups. How many altogether?
(25)

Suppose there are this number in each of 2 groups. How many altogether?
(10)

Show a number card 1–10 to represent the number in each of 2 or 5 groups.

Day 10

Show a number card such as 4.

Suppose there are this number in each of 5 groups. How many altogether?
(20)

Suppose there are this number in each of 2 groups. How many altogether?
(8)

Show a number card 1–10 to represent the number in each of 2 or 5 groups.

Double Trouble

Summary

Students use LinkerCubes® to model facts. They describe each display they make with a doubles fact for addition and a multiplication fact that begins with the factor two.

Materials

Each pair of students needs

▶ One (1) copy of Double Trouble, page 31

▶ Twenty (20) LinkerCubes®

Directions

❶ Demonstrate placing three cubes in each of two squares on the overhead projector.

❷ Write an addition fact and a multiplication fact that describes the display.

❸ Have students work in pairs to complete Double Trouble, page 31.

Talk About It

Ask students to discuss their observations.

What patterns did you find in the pairs of addition and multiplication facts? (A number plus itself is equal to two groups of the same number.)

How could you use these patterns to help you remember multiplication facts that have 2 as a factor? (If you know your addition doubles facts, you can use them to find the answers to facts that have 2 as a factor.)

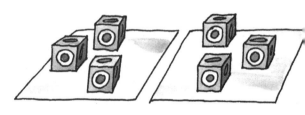

$$3 + 3 = 6$$
$$2 \times 3 = 6$$

Double Trouble

Use LinkerCubes® to create displays that can be described with addition and multiplication facts. Look for patterns.

Directions

❶ Follow the instructions for each exercise and place cubes in the spaces provided.

❷ Write an addition fact and a multiplication fact that describes your display.

❸ Turn this paper over and use the back to describe the patterns you find.

❹ Explain how the addition and multiplication facts are related.

1. **Put 5 cubes in each space.**

_____ + _____ = _____

_____ × _____ = _____

2. **Put 4 cubes in each space.**

_____ + _____ = _____

_____ × _____ = _____

3. **Put 7 cubes in each space.**

_____ + _____ = _____

_____ × _____ = _____

4. **Put 6 cubes in each space.**

_____ + _____ = _____

_____ × _____ = _____

Permission is given by the publisher to reproduce this page for classroom or home use only.

Nickels and Dimes

Summary

Students model multiplying-5 facts with nickels. They exchange nickels for dimes and discuss patterns.

Materials

Each pair of students needs

▶ One (1) copy of Nickels and Dimes, page 33

▶ Play money, ten (10) nickels and five (5) dimes

Directions

Have students work in pairs to complete Nickels and Dimes, page 33.

Talk About It

Write eleven complete multiplying-5 facts on the board, in order, from $0 \times 5 = 0$ to $10 \times 5 = 50$.

What patterns do you notice when the complete facts that have 5 as a factor are written? (The multiples end with a zero or a five. Accept all correct responses.)

How can you use the patterns found to remember your multiplying-5 facts? (Accept reasonable answers.)

Extension Ask students to write a clear, brief rule for remembering multiplying-5 facts. This is not an easy assignment. Allow students time to share their ideas with each other and to revise their rules to improve their wording.

Nickels and Dimes

Use nickels to model facts for multiplying-5 facts. Trade nickels for dimes and record the exchanges. What patterns can you find?

Directions

1 Take nickels to match the number in the first column.

2 Write a complete multiplication fact that describes your collection of nickels.

3 Trade in nickels to get dimes.

4 Record the number of dimes and nickels you have after the trade.

5 On the back of this paper, write all eleven multiplying-5 facts, in order, starting with 0×5 and ending with 10×5. Write the product for each fact.

6 Describe any patterns you see. Describe a way to remember facts for multiplying-5.

Number of Nickels	Multiplication Facts	After Exchange	
		Number of Dimes	Number of Nickels
3	$3 \times 5 = 15$	1	1
4			
7			
8			
5			
9			

Doubles and Five-0s

Practice

Work on these sets of practice exercises until students get each answer within three (3) seconds. Ask students to state the entire fact rather than just the answer ("2 × 5 = 10" instead of "10"). Stating the complete fact improves students' recall. Present the facts in various ways. Ask the students to listen and then reply verbally, or use flash cards and have the students write their facts. Varying the format helps all students focus on the facts.

Talk About It

Ask students to talk about their thinking. Follow up by asking if anyone has a way to remember his or her facts which is different than the methods already discussed.

How do you find the product for a multiplication fact that has 2 as a factor?
(Answers might include that multiples of 2 are even numbers and that they are the same as the addition doubles facts. Accept all reasonable answers.)

How do remember your multiplying-5 facts?
(Answers might include that multiples of 5 have a zero or a five in the ones place. Accept all reasonable answers.)

Day 1

Present these facts.

8 × 2 (16)	2 × 2 (4)
1 × 2 (2)	9 × 2 (18)
5 × 2 (10)	2 × 1 (2)
3 × 2 (6)	2 × 3 (6)
7 × 2 (14)	4 × 2 (8)
2 × 9 (18)	10 × 2 (20)
2 × 8 (16)	2 × 5 (10)
2 × 6 (12)	2 × 7 (14)
0 × 2 (0)	2 × 4 (8)
6 × 2 (12)	2 × 10 (20)

Extension Present facts that have any number 0–20 as one factor and 2 as the second factor. Be sure to vary the order of the factors.

Day 2

Present these facts.

2 × 10 (20)	6 × 2 (12)
2 × 4 (8)	0 × 2 (0)
2 × 7 (14)	2 × 6 (12)
2 × 5 (10)	2 × 8 (16)
10 × 2 (20)	2 × 9 (18)
4 × 2 (8)	7 × 2 (14)
2 × 3 (6)	3 × 2 (6)
2 × 1 (2)	5 × 2 (10)
9 × 2 (18)	1 × 2 (2)
2 × 2 (4)	8 × 2 (16)

Extension Present facts that have any number 0–20 as one factor and 2 as the second factor. Be sure to vary the order of the factors.

Day 3

Present these facts.

0 × 5 (0)	1 × 5 (5)
2 × 5 (10)	5 × 3 (15)
8 × 5 (40)	5 × 10 (50)
7 × 5 (35)	5 × 7 (35)
5 × 5 (25)	9 × 5 (45)
5 × 2 (10)	10 × 5 (50)
6 × 5 (30)	5 × 1 (5)
5 × 9 (45)	5 × 6 (30)
4 × 5 (20)	3 × 5 (15)
5 × 8 (40)	5 × 4 (20)

Extension Present facts that have any number 0–20 as one factor and 5 as the second factor. Be sure to vary the order of the factors.

Day 4

Present these facts.

5 × 8 (40)	5 × 4 (20)
4 × 5 (20)	3 × 5 (15)
5 × 9 (45)	5 × 6 (30)
6 × 5 (30)	5 × 1 (5)
5 × 2 (10)	10 × 5 (50)
5 × 5 (25)	9 × 5 (45)
7 × 5 (35)	5 × 7 (35)
8 × 5 (40)	5 × 10 (50)
2 × 5 (10)	5 × 3 (15)
0 × 5 (0)	1 × 5 (5)

Extension Present facts that have any number 0–20 as one factor and 5 as the second factor. Be sure to vary the order of the factors.

Day 5

Present these facts.

2 × 1 (2)	2 × 4 (8)
5 × 0 (0)	5 × 9 (45)
2 × 5 (10)	4 × 5 (20)
2 × 3 (6)	2 × 10 (20)
4 × 2 (8)	1 × 5 (5)
8 × 5 (40)	5 × 3 (15)
10 × 2 (20)	8 × 2 (16)
5 × 5 (30)	1 × 2 (2)
6 × 5 (30)	5 × 10 (50)
2 × 7 (14)	5 × 7 (35)

Extension Present facts that have any number 0–20 as one factor and 2 or 5 as the second factor. Be sure to vary the order of the factors.

Day 6

Present these facts.

9 × 2 (18)	7 × 2 (14)
2 × 2 (4)	2 × 5 (10)
5 × 4 (20)	5 × 5 (25)
3 × 5 (15)	10 × 5 (50)
2 × 10 (20)	6 × 2 (12)
2 × 4 (8)	2 × 0 (0)
5 × 0 (0)	5 × 9 (45)
8 × 2 (16)	3 × 5 (15)
1 × 5 (5)	3 × 2 (6)
2 × 1 (2)	4 × 5 (20)

Extension Present facts that have any number 0–20 as one factor and 2 or 5 as the second factor. Be sure to vary the order of the factors.

Day 7

Present these facts.

8 × 2 (16)	6 × 5 (30)
5 × 2 (10)	5 × 9 (45)
7 × 2 (14)	6 × 2 (12)
2 × 9 (18)	9 × 2 (18)
2 × 8 (16)	5 × 8 (40)
2 × 6 (12)	5 × 4 (20)
8 × 5 (40)	2 × 0 (0)
7 × 5 (35)	2 × 7 (14)
5 × 5 (25)	5 × 6 (30)
5 × 2 (10)	9 × 5 (45)

Extension Present facts that have any number 0–20 as one factor and 2 or 5 as the second factor. Be sure to vary the order of the factors.

Day 8

Present these facts.

5 × 9 (45)	2 × 7 (14)
6 × 5 (30)	5 × 6 (30)
5 × 2 (10)	9 × 5 (45)
5 × 5 (25)	8 × 5 (40)
7 × 5 (35)	2 × 6 (12)
6 × 2 (12)	2 × 8 (16)
9 × 2 (18)	2 × 9 (18)
5 × 8 (40)	7 × 2 (14)
5 × 4 (20)	5 × 2 (10)
2 × 10 (20)	8 × 2 (16)

Extension Present facts that have any number 0 to 20 as one factor and 2 or 5 as the second factor. Be sure to vary the order of the factors.

Day 9

Pose these questions.

How much money do you have with

3 nickels? (15¢)

8 nickels? (40¢)

5 nickels? (25¢)

7 nickels? (35¢)

4 nickels? (20¢)

6 nickels? (30¢)

9 nickels? (45¢)

Extension Continue this activity but have the number of nickels exceed 10.

Day 10

Pose these questions.

How many minutes is it after the hour when the minute hand is on the

2? (10 minutes)

5? (25 minutes)

7? (35 minutes)

9? (45 minutes)

4? (20 minutes)

3? (15 minutes)

10? (50 minutes)

11? (55 minutes)

Extension List things that come in sets of five, like fingers on one hand, and ask students to tell how many individual items there would be in different numbers of sets.

Patterns with Nines Overview

What are the Patterns with Nines?

Patterns with nines focuses students attention on various patterns that exist in the multiples of nine. These patterns will help students to remember the facts.

Patterns include:

▶ The sum of the digits of multiples of nine is always nine.

▶ The tens digit of the product is one less than the factor being multiplied by nine.

▶ When the multiples of nine are listed in order from least to greatest, the tens digits increase by one and the ones digits decrease by one with each product listed.

When to Use Patterns with Nines

Use this strategy with multiplication facts that have nine as one of the factors.

×	0	1	2	3	4	5	6	7	8	9	10
0										0	
1										9	
2										18	
3										28	
4										36	
5										45	
6										54	
7										63	
8										72	
9	0	9	18	27	36	45	54	63	72	81	90
10										90	

Prerequisites

Students should understand multiplication concepts (pages viii-1). They should be able to identify and describe numeric patterns.

Additional Experiences

Have students shade multiples of nine on a hundred chart. Then ask students to describe the patterns they find.

1	2	3	4	5	6	7	8	9	10
11	12	13	14	15	16	17	18	19	20
21	22	23	24	25	26	27	28	29	30
31	32	33	34	35	36	37	38	39	40
41	42	43	44	45	46	47	48	49	50
51	52	53	54	55	56	57	58	59	60
61	62	63	64	65	66	67	68	69	70
71	72	73	74	75	76	77	78	79	80
81	82	83	84	85	86	87	88	89	90
91	92	93	94	95	96	97	98	99	100

You can find additional practice in *Practice Your Facts, Levels 1–5,* by Creative Publications, Inc.

Patterns with Nines

Warm-ups

Each warm-up exercise set should take two (2) or three (3) minutes. The short sets of exercises are great for filling transition times. Some teachers use them while students stand in line.

Talk About It

As you work through these warm-ups, ask students to talk about their thinking. This not only helps you assess, but gives students a chance to clarify their thinking and to hear about ways of thinking that might be different from theirs. You might ask questions like

Choose a multiple of 9. Add the digits. Choose another multiple of 9 and add the digits. What do you notice? (The sum of the digits is 9 in both cases.)

Does this happen with all of the multiples of 9? (Yes. If the sum of the digits of a multiple of 9 is greater than 9, add the digits in the sum.)

What do you notice when the multiples of 9 are written in order? (From one multiple to the next, the tens digit increases by one and the ones digit decreases by one.)

A great question to keep the discussion going is

Does anyone have any different answers?

Day 1

Ask students to count as directed.

Count by 9. Start with 9 and count to 90.
(9, 18, 27, 36, 45, 54, 63, 72, 81, 90)

Repeat until most students can count quickly and accurately.

Day 2

Ask students to count as directed.

Count by 9. Start with 9 and count 6 times.
(9, 18, 27, 36, 45, 54)

What are six 9s?
(54)

Count by 9. Start with 9 and count 4 times.
(9, 18, 27, 36)

What are four 9s?
(36)

Continue to have students count by 9 from 1–10 times.

Day 3

Ask students to count as directed.

Count by 9. Start with 9 and count 2 times.
(9, 18)

What are two 9s?
(18)

Count by 9. Start with 9 and count 9 times.
(9, 18, 27, 36, 45, 54, 63, 72, 81)

What are nine 9s? (81)

Continue to have students count by 9 from 1–10 times.

Day 4

Pose these questions.

Suppose there are 5 bananas on each of 9 trays. How many bananas altogether?
(45 bananas)

Suppose there are 9 fish in each of 8 fish tanks. How many fish altogether?
(72 fish)

Continue to present situations with 9 items in each of 1–10 groups asking

How many altogether?

Day 5

Pose these questions.

Suppose there are 9 flowers in each of 3 vases. How many flowers altogether?
(27 flowers)

Suppose there are 9 pieces of chicken on each of 6 plates. How many pieces of chicken altogether?
(54 pieces of chicken)

Continue to present situations with 9 items in each of 1–10 groups, asking

How many altogether?

Patterns with Nines

Summary

Students look for patterns in the products of facts that have nine as a factor. Using those patterns will make remembering the facts easier.

Individual Activity

Materials

One (1) copy of Patterns with Nines, page 44, for each student

Directions

❶ Have students complete Patterns with Nines, page 44.

❷ Encourage students to discuss their findings with each other to stimulate identifying additional patterns.

Talk About It

Write the facts multiplying-9 facts and their products on the board.

$$0 \times 9 = 0$$
$$1 \times 9 = 9$$
$$2 \times 9 = 18$$
$$3 \times 9 = 27$$
$$4 \times 9 = 36$$
$$5 \times 9 = 45$$
$$6 \times 9 = 54$$
$$7 \times 9 = 63$$
$$8 \times 9 = 72$$
$$9 \times 9 = 81$$
$$10 \times 9 = 90$$

Discuss the patterns that students found.

What patterns did you find in the facts that have nine as a factor?
(Accept all reasonable answers.) List the patterns in a separate place on the board.

Did anyone find a pattern that has not been discussed? (Accept all accurate responses.)

How can we use the patterns we found to help us remember the multiplying-9 facts?
(Accept all accurate responses.)

Extension or Homework

Use At Your Fingertips, page 45, to teach your students how to use their fingers to remember their multiplying-9 facts. This method employs the fact that the sum of the digits of a multiple of 9 is 9. When one finger is bent down, nine fingers remain unbent.

This method also uses the pattern of the tens digit always being one less than the factor being multiplied by nine. When the finger corresponding to the factor multiplying nine is bent down, the fingers to the left of the bent finger automatically become one less than the number represented by that finger.

note To find the product of a larger fact such as 18 × 9 using the finger method, students can separate 18 into 10 + 8 and follow these steps:

First, use fingers to find 10 × 9 (90).

Next, use fingers to find 8 × 9 (72). Start with 90 and count on, counting by ten, the fingers representing tens in 72 to reach 160.

Finally, add 2 for the fingers representing ones in 72 to reach 162.

Patterns with Nines

Find as many patterns as you can in the list of multiplying-9 facts and their products.

$0 \times 9 = 0$

$1 \times 9 = 9$

$2 \times 9 = 18$

$3 \times 9 = 27$

$4 \times 9 = 36$

$5 \times 9 = 45$

$6 \times 9 = 54$

$7 \times 9 = 63$

$8 \times 9 = 72$

$9 \times 9 = 81$

$10 \times 9 = 90$

Directions

❶ Describe the patterns you find on the lines below.

❷ Turn this paper over and write the facts from 11×9 through 20×9 on the back. Write the product for each fact.

❸ Describe how any of the patterns you found can work for these facts.

❹ Write about any new patterns you find.

_____

_____

_____

_____

_____

_____

At Your Fingertips

Have your multiplying-9 facts at your fingertips!

Directions

1 Hold your hands in front of you, palms down. Assign a number to each finger.

2 Bend down the finger that represents the factor multiplying nine.

3 The open fingers to the left of the bent finger represent the tens place of the product. The fingers to the right of the bent finger represent the ones place of the product.

4 Try the fingertip method with other multiplying-9 facts.

5 Can you use this method to find products when the factor multiplying nine is greater than ten? If so, explain how.

Patterns with Nines

Practice

Work on these sets of practice exercises until students can get each answer within three (3) seconds. Ask students to tell the whole fact rather than just the answer ("3 × 9 = 27" instead of "27"). When students tell the whole fact, it improves their recall. Try presenting the facts in various ways. Ask the students to listen and reply verbally, or use flash cards and have the students write their facts. Varying the format helps all students focus on the facts.

Talk About It

Ask students to talk about their thinking. Follow up by asking if anyone has a different way to find the answer.

How do you remember your multiplying-9 facts? (Accept all reasonable methods.)

Describe a rule that helps you figure out multiplying-9 facts. (Answers might include that the sum of the digits in the product equals nine, that the tens digit is one less than the factor multiplying nine, or using the fingertip method. Accept all reasonable responses.)

Day 1
Present these facts.

0 × 9 (0)	9 × 0 (0)
9 × 9 (81)	6 × 9 (54)
5 × 9 (45)	9 × 2 (18)
9 × 3 (27)	1 × 9 (9)
8 × 9 (72)	9 × 4 (36)
9 × 6 (54)	9 × 1 (9)
2 × 9 (18)	7 × 9 (63)
9 × 8 (72)	3 × 9 (27)
10 × 9 (90)	9 × 10 (90)
9 × 9 (36)	9 × 5 (45)
4 × 9 (81)	9 × 7 (63)

Extension Present facts that have a number 11–15 as one factor and 9 as the second factor. Be sure to vary the order of the factors.

Day 2
Present these facts.

9 × 8 (72)	3 × 9 (27)
9 × 4 (36)	8 × 9 (72)
0 × 9 (0)	9 × 0 (0)
9 × 9 (81)	9 × 10 (90)
10 × 9 (90)	9 × 6 (54)
9 × 1 (9)	6 × 9 (54)
5 × 9 (45)	9 × 5 (45)
9 × 9 (81)	2 × 9 (18)
7 × 9 (63)	9 × 7 (63)
9 × 3 (27)	9 × 2 (18)
4 × 9 (36)	1 × 9 (9)

Extension Present facts that have a number 11–15 as one factor and 9 as the second factor. Be sure to vary the order of the factors.

Day 3

Present these facts.

9 × 10 (90)	9 × 1 (9)
1 × 9 (9)	9 × 0 (0)
9 × 9 (81)	2 × 9 (18)
8 × 9 (72)	5 × 9 (45)
0 × 9 (0)	7 × 9 (63)
9 × 5 (45)	6 × 9 (54)
9 × 4 (36)	9 × 8 (72)
9 × 6 (54)	9 × 3 (27)
9 × 9 (81)	10 × 9 (90)
9 × 7 (63)	9 × 2 (18)
4 × 9 (36)	3 × 9 (27)

Extension Present facts that have a number 11–20 as one factor and 9 as the second factor. Be sure to vary the order of the factors.

Day 4

Present these facts.

8 × 9 (72)	9 × 1 (9)
9 × 3 (27)	9 × 4 (36)
5 × 9 (45)	1 × 9 (9)
9 × 9 (81)	9 × 2 (18)
0 × 9 (0)	6 × 9 (54)
4 × 9 (36)	9 × 0 (0)
9 × 9 (81)	9 × 7 (63)
10 × 9 (90)	9 × 5 (45)
9 × 8 (72)	9 × 10 (90)
2 × 9 (18)	3 × 9 (27)
9 × 6 (54)	7 × 9 (63)

Extension Present facts that have a number 11–15 as one factor and 9 as the second factor. Be sure to vary the order of the factors.

Day 5

Present these facts.

9 × 11 (99)	6 × 9 (54)
9 × 9 (81)	11 × 9 (99)
5 × 9 (45)	9 × 4 (36)
8 × 9 (72)	9 × 12 (108)
7 × 9 (63)	9 × 6 (54)
12 × 9 (108)	20 × 9 (180)
9 × 10 (90)	9 × 8 (72)
9 × 5 (45)	10 × 9 (90)
9 × 7 (63)	9 × 9 (81)
9 × 100 (900)	4 × 9 (36)

Extension Present facts that have a number 11–15 as one factor and 9 as the second factor. Be sure to vary the order of the factors.

Counting Threes Overview

What is Counting Threes?

Students use their ability to count by three to remember their multiplying-with-3 facts.

When to Use Counting Threes

Use counting threes with multiplication facts that have three as a factor.

Prerequisites

Students should understand subtraction concepts (pages viii-1). They should be able to count by three to thirty.

×	0	1	2	3	4	5	6	7	8	9	10
0				0							
1				3							
2				6							
3	0	3	6	9	12	15	18	21	24	27	30
4				12							
5				15							
6				18							
7				21							
8				24							
9				27							
10				30							

Additional Experiences

Have students count by three frequently. One way to practice is to have pairs of students do three-step clapping patterns. With the first step, students clap with their partner, right hand to right hand. With the second step, they clap with their partner, left hand to left hand. With the third step, students clap their own hands. As they clap, students count—softly as they clap hands with their partners and louder when they clap their own hands. The louder numbers are multiples of three. It is an interesting challenge to see if your whole class can do this simultaneously.

You can find additional practice in *Practice Your Facts, Levels 1–5,* by Creative Publications, Inc.

Counting Threes

Warm-ups

Each warm-up exercise set should take two (2) or three (3) minutes. The short sets of exercises are great for filling transition times. Some teachers use them while students stand in line.

Talk About It

As you work through these warm-ups, ask students to talk about their thinking. This not only helps you assess, but gives students a chance to clarify their thinking and to hear about ways of thinking that might be different from theirs. You might ask questions like

Twelve is a multiple of 3. Write 12 on the board.

What sum do we get when we add the digits of 12? (3) Demonstrate by writing $1 + 2 = 3$.

Twenty-four is another multiple of 3. Write 24 on the board.

What sum do we get when we add the digits of 24? (6) Demonstrate.

Eighteen is also a multiple of 3. Write 18 on the board.

What sum do we get when we add the digits of 18? (9) Demonstrate.

Choose other multiples of 3 that have two digits and find the sum of the digits. What do you notice? (The sum of the digits is 3, 6, or 9 in all cases.)

Does this happen with all of the multiples of 3? (Yes. If digits in a multiple of 3 have a sum greater than 3, add the digits in the sum. For example, $3 \times 13 = 39$, $3 + 9 = 12$, and $1 + 2 = 3$.)

Day 1

Ask students to count as directed.

Count by 3. Count to 30.
(3, 6, 9, 12, 15, 18, 21, 24, 27, 30)

Repeat until most students can count quickly and accurately.

Day 2

Ask students to count as directed.

Count by 3. Start with 3 and count 7 times.
(3, 6, 9, 12, 15, 18, 21)

What are seven 3s?
(21)

Count by 3. Start with 3 and count 1 time.
(3)

What is one 3?
(3)

Continue to have students count by 3 any number 1–10 times.

Day 3

Ask students to count as directed.

Count by 3. Start with 3 and count 4 times.
(3, 6, 9, 12)

What are four 3s?
(12)

Count by 3. Start with 3 and count 10 times.
(3, 6, 9, 12, 15, 18, 21, 24, 27, 30)

Continue to have students count by 3 any number 1–10 times.

Day 4

Ask students to count as directed.

Count by 9. Start with 9 and count 3 times.
(9, 18, 27)

What are three 9s?
(27)

Count by 6. Start with 6 and count 3 times.
(6, 12, 18)

What are three 6s?
(18)

Continue to have students count by any number 1–10 three times.

Day 5

Ask students to count as directed.

Count by 2. Start with 2 and count 3 times.
(2, 4, 6)

What are three 2s?
(6)

Count by 5. Start with 5 and count 3 times.
(5, 10, 15)

Continue to have students count by any number 1–10 three times.

Day 6

Write numbers on the board as indicated.

3 + 3 + 3 + 3

What multiplication fact and product describes these numbers? $(4 \times 3 = 12)$

3 + 3 + 3 + 3 + 3

What multiplication fact and product describes these numbers? $(5 \times 3 = 15)$

Continue to write 10 or fewer 3s and ask students to describe what you have written with a multiplication fact and product.

Day 7

Pose these questions.

Suppose there are 3 wheels on each of 2 tricycles. How many wheels altogether?
(6 wheels)

Suppose there are 3 stamps on each of 6 envelopes. How many stamps altogether?
(18 stamps)

Continue to present situations with 3 items in each of 1–10 groups, asking

How many altogether?

Day 8

Pose these questions.

Suppose there are 3 doors on each of 9 buildings. How many doors altogether?
(27 doors)

Suppose there are 3 eyes on each of 8 alien beings. How many eyes altogether?
(24 eyes)

Continue to present situations with 3 items in each of 1–10 groups, asking

How many altogether?

Day 9

Pose these questions.

Suppose there are 5 members on each of 3 teams. How many members altogether?
(15 members)

Suppose there is 1 computer in each of 3 classrooms. How many computers altogether?
(3 computers)

Continue to present situations with 1–10 items in each of 3 groups, asking

How many altogether?

Day 10

Pose these questions.

Suppose there are 3 chairs at each of 3 tables. How many chairs altogether?
(9 chairs)

Suppose there are 3 slices of pizza on each of 4 plates. How many slices of pizza altogether?
(12 slices of pizza)

Continue to present situations with 3 items in each of 1–10 groups, asking

How many altogether?

Multiples of Three

Summary

Students examine a list of multiples of three to find patterns. Then they discuss how the patterns found can help them remember the multiplying-3 facts.

Preparation

Prepare a hundred chart for the overhead by shading multiples of three. Alternatively, make the chart on the board or on poster paper large enough to be seen by all students.

Materials

One (1) copy of Multiples of Three, page 56, for each student

Directions

❶ Allow students about ten minutes to work independently on Multiples of Three, page 56.

❷ Encourage students to discuss their findings with each other. This should stimulate students to find additional patterns.

1	2	3	4	5	6	7	8	9	10
11	12	13	14	15	16	17	18	19	20
21	22	23	24	25	26	27	28	29	30
31	32	33	34	35	36	37	38	39	40
41	42	43	44	45	46	47	48	49	50
51	52	53	54	55	56	57	58	59	60
61	62	63	64	65	66	67	68	69	70
71	72	73	74	75	76	77	78	79	80
81	82	83	84	85	86	87	88	89	90
91	92	93	94	95	96	97	98	99	100

Talk About It

Show students the hundred chart with multiples of three pre-shaded. Ask

What patterns did you find when you looked at the multiples of three on the hundred chart? (Answers might include that shaded squares representing multiples of 3 form diagonal lines; there are two unshaded spaces horizontally and vertically between shaded spaces; and the digits of each number along a diagonal add up to the same number—either 3, 6, or 9. Accept all accurate responses.)

How could you use some of the patterns the class found to help remember your multiplying-3 facts? (Accept all reasonable responses.)

Extension or Homework

Each student will need a copy of Growing Threes, page 57, and crayons. Instruct students to first complete the table and then work in order to color one column for each product. Working with multiples of three in this fashion will help students visualize the facts.

Multiples of Three

Find as many patterns as you can in the multiples of 3. These patterns can help you remember the multiplying-3 facts.

Directions

❶ Shade the squares that contain multiples of 3. Color lightly so that you can still see the number.

❷ On a separate piece of paper, write about the patterns you see.

1	2	3	4	5	6	7	8	9	10
11	12	13	14	15	16	17	18	19	20
21	22	23	24	25	26	27	28	29	30
31	32	33	34	35	36	37	38	39	40
41	42	43	44	45	46	47	48	49	50
51	52	53	54	55	56	57	58	59	60
61	62	63	64	65	66	67	68	69	70
71	72	73	74	75	76	77	78	79	80
81	82	83	84	85	86	87	88	89	90
91	92	93	94	95	96	97	98	99	100

Growing Threes

Watch the threes grow!

Directions

1. Complete the table.

2. Color a single column to match each product. Go in order.

0	0 × 3	0
1	1 × 3	3
2		
	3 × 3	
		12
5		
		18
	7 × 3	
8		
		27
10		

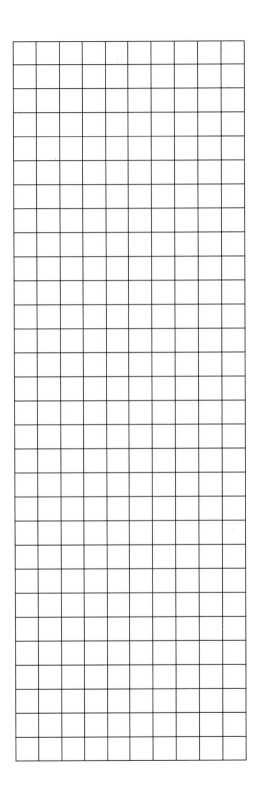

Counting Threes

Practice

Work on these sets of practice problems until students can get each answer within three (3) seconds. Ask students to tell the whole fact rather than just the answer ("3 × 5 = 15" instead of "15"). When students tell the whole fact, it improves their recall. Try presenting the facts in various ways. Ask the students to listen and reply verbally, or use flash cards and have the students write their facts. Varying the format helps all students focus on the facts.

Talk About It

Ask students to talk about their thinking.

Do you have a way to remember the multiplying-3 facts? (Accept all accurate methods.)

Does anyone have another way to remember these facts? (Accept all accurate methods.)

Day 1

Present these facts.

3 × 3 (9)	3 × 4 (12)
9 × 3 (27)	10 × 3 (30)
3 × 7 (21)	0 × 3 (0)
1 × 3 (3)	2 × 3 (6)
3 × 5 (15)	3 × 1 (3)
6 × 3 (18)	3 × 8 (24)
3 × 3 (3)	3 × 10 (30)
7 × 3 (21)	3 × 6 (18)
3 × 2 (6)	5 × 3 (15)
3 × 0 (0)	3 × 9 (27)
8 × 3 (24)	4 × 3 (12)

Extension Present facts that have 3 as one factor and numbers 10–15, in order, as the second factor.

Day 2

Present these facts.

3 × 2 (6)	7 × 3 (21)
3 × 0 (0)	0 × 3 (0)
8 × 3 (24)	10 × 3 (30)
3 × 4 (12)	3 × 1 (3)
9 × 3 (27)	1 × 3 (3)
6 × 3 (18)	3 × 7 (21)
3 × 8 (24)	3 × 3 (9)
5 × 3 (15)	3 × 10 (30)
3 × 3 (3)	3 × 6 (18)
3 × 5 (15)	3 × 9 (27)
2 × 3 (6)	4 × 3 (12)

Extension Present facts that have 3 as one factor and numbers 10–15, in order, as the second factor.

Day 3

Present these facts.

3 × 0 (0)	2 × 3 (6)
3 × 2 (6)	10 × 3 (30)
3 × 4 (12)	0 × 3 (0)
8 × 3 (24)	1 × 3 (3)
6 × 3 (18)	3 × 1 (3)
9 × 3 (27)	3 × 3 (9)
5 × 3 (15)	3 × 7 (21)
3 × 8 (24)	3 × 6 (18)
3 × 5 (15)	3 × 10 (30)
3 × 3 (3)	4 × 3 (12)
7 × 3 (21)	3 × 9 (27)

Extension Present facts that have 3 as one factor and any number 1–15 as the second factor.

Day 4

Present these facts.

3 × 2 (6)	1 × 3 (3)
3 × 0 (0)	3 × 3 (9)
3 × 4 (12)	3 × 1 (3)
3 × 8 (24)	3 × 7 (21)
5 × 3 (15)	7 × 3 (21)
3 × 5 (15)	3 × 3 (9)
6 × 3 (18)	2 × 3 (6)
8 × 3 (24)	3 × 10 (30)
9 × 3 (27)	3 × 6 (18)
0 × 3 (0)	4 × 3 (12)
10 × 3 (30)	3 × 9 (27)

Extension Present facts that have 3 as one factor and a multiple of 10 (limit 100) as the second factor.

....

Day 5

Present these facts.

3 × 10 (30)	7 × 3 (21)
3 × 7 (21)	3 × 1 (3)
3 × 3 (9)	0 × 3 (0)
3 × 6 (18)	10 × 3 (30)
8 × 3 (24)	1 × 3 (3)
3 × 2 (6)	3 × 8 (24)
3 × 0 (0)	9 × 3 (27)
3 × 4 (12)	6 × 3 (18)
2 × 3 (6)	5 × 3 (15)
3 × 3 (3)	3 × 9 (27)
3 × 5 (15)	4 × 3 (12)

Extension Present facts that have 3 as one factor and any number 1–15 as the second factor.

....

Day 7

Present these facts.

3 × 7 (21)	3 × 9 (27)
8 × 3 (24)	3 × 4 (12)
3 × 6 (18)	3 × 5 (15)
0 × 3 (0)	3 × 3 (9)
3 × 8 (24)	3 × 10 (30)
1 × 3 (3)	3 × 3 (9)
3 × 1 (3)	3 × 2 (6)
10 × 3 (30)	3 × 0 (0)
9 × 3 (27)	2 × 3 (6)
5 × 3 (15)	7 × 3 (21)
4 × 3 (12)	6 × 3 (18)

Extension Present facts that have 3 as one factor and a multiple of 1,000 as the second factor.

....

Day 6

Present these facts.

3 × 7 (21)	10 × 3 (30)
3 × 6 (18)	3 × 4 (12)
8 × 3 (24)	3 × 11 (33)
3 × 10 (30)	3 × 5 (15)
3 × 2 (6)	3 × 0 (0)
3 × 3 (9)	7 × 3 (21)
0 × 3 (0)	2 × 3 (6)
1 × 3 (3)	5 × 3 (15)
3 × 8 (24)	3 × 9 (27)
3 × 1 (3)	4 × 3 (12)
9 × 3 (27)	6 × 3 (18)

Extension Present facts that have 3 as one factor and a multiple of 100 (limit 1,000) as the second factor.

Day 8

Present these facts.

5 × 3 (15)	4 × 3 (12)
9 × 3 (27)	3 × 5 (15)
10 × 3 (30)	3 × 4 (12)
3 × 1 (3)	3 × 10 (30)
8 × 3 (24)	3 × 11 (33)
3 × 7 (21)	3 × 2 (6)
0 × 3 (0)	3 × 3 (9)
3 × 6 (18)	2 × 3 (6)
1 × 3 (3)	3 × 0 (0)
3 × 8 (24)	6 × 3 (18)
3 × 9 (27)	7 × 3 (21)

Extension Present facts that have 3 as one factor and a multiple of 10, 100, or 1,000 as the second factor.

Day 9

Present these facts.

9 × 3 (27)	4 × 3 (12)
5 × 3 (15)	3 × 4 (12)
10 × 3 (30)	3 × 5 (15)
8 × 3 (24)	3 × 10 (30)
3 × 1 (3)	3 × 2 (6)
3 × 7 (21)	3 × 11 (33)
3 × 6 (18)	3 × 3 (9)
0 × 3 (0)	3 × 0 (0)
1 × 3 (3)	2 × 3 (6)
3 × 9 (27)	6 × 3 (18)
3 × 8 (24)	7 × 3 (21)

Extension Present facts that have 3 as one factor and a multiple of 25 as the second factor.

Day 10

Present these facts.

3 × 3 (9)	5 × 3 (15)
3 × 11 (33)	8 × 3 (24)
3 × 0 (0)	3 × 1 (3)
2 × 3 (6)	9 × 3 (27)
3 × 2 (6)	0 × 3 (0)
3 × 4 (12)	3 × 6 (18)
4 × 3 (12)	1 × 3 (3)
3 × 5 (15)	3 × 9 (27)
3 × 10 (30)	3 × 7 (21)
3 × 8 (24)	7 × 3 (21)
10 × 3 (30)	6 × 3 (18)

Extension Present facts that have 3 as one factor and a multiple of 25, 100, or 1,000 as the second factor.

Splitting Fours

What is Splitting Fours?

With splitting fours, students split a fact with a factor of 4 into two equal multiply-2 facts which are easier to solve. They then find the product of a multiply-2 fact and double it. For example, $4 \times 7 =$ double $2 \times 7 =$ double $14 = 28$.

When to Use Splitting Fours

Use splitting fours with multiplication facts that have four as a factor.

Prerequisites

Students should understand multiplication concepts (pages viii-1). They should also know their multiply-by-2 facts and be able to double any number up to 20.

×	0	1	2	3	4	5	6	7	8	9	10
0					0						
1					4						
2					8						
3					12						
4	0	4	8	12	16	20	24	28	32	36	40
5					20						
6					24						
7					28						
8					32						
9					36						
10					40						

Additional Experiences

Have students shade a hundred chart with multiples of two and another with multiples of four. Ask students to find similarities between the two charts. Have students compare the products that result when multiplying two and four by the same number. Students will be able to observe that multiples of four are doubles of the multiples of two.

You can find additional practice in *Practice Your Facts, Levels 1–5,* by Creative Publications, Inc.

1	2	3	4	5	6	7	8	9	10
11	12	13	14	15	16	17	18	19	20
21	22	23	24	25	26	27	28	29	30
31	32	33	34	35	36	37	38	39	40
41	42	43	44	45	46	47	48	49	50
51	52	53	54	55	56	57	58	59	60
61	62	63	64	65	66	67	68	69	70
71	72	73	74	75	76	77	78	79	80
81	82	83	84	85	86	87	88	89	90
91	92	93	94	95	96	97	98	99	100

1	2	3	4	5	6	7	8	9	10
11	12	13	14	15	16	17	18	19	20
21	22	23	24	25	26	27	28	29	30
31	32	33	34	35	36	37	38	39	40
41	42	43	44	45	46	47	48	49	50
51	52	53	54	55	56	57	58	59	60
61	62	63	64	65	66	67	68	69	70
71	72	73	74	75	76	77	78	79	80
81	82	83	84	85	86	87	88	89	90
91	92	93	94	95	96	97	98	99	100

Splitting Fours

Warm-ups

Each warm-up exercise set should take two (2) or three (3) minutes. The short sets of exercises are great for filling transition times. Some teachers use them while students stand in line.

Talk About It

As you work through these warm-ups, ask students to talk about their thinking. This not only helps you assess, but gives students a chance to clarify their thinking and to hear about ways of thinking that might be different from theirs. You might ask questions like

What do you notice about the multiples of 4?
(Answers might include that they are all even numbers and that they are also multiples of two. Accept all accurate responses.)

....

Day 1

Ask students to count as directed.

Count by 4. Start with 4 and count to 40.
(4, 8, 12, 16, 20, 24, 28, 32, 36, 40)

Repeat until most students can count quickly and accurately.

....

Day 2

Ask students to count as directed.

Count by 4. Start with 4 and count 7 times.
(4, 8, 12, 16, 20, 24, 28)

What are seven 4s?
(28)

Count by 4. Start with 4 and count 3 times.
(4, 8, 12)

What are three 4s?
(12)

Continue to have students count by 4 from 1–10 times.

Day 3

Ask students to count as directed.

Count by 5. Start with 5 and count 4 times.
(5, 10, 15, 20)

What are four 5s?
(20)

Count by 9. Start with 9 and count 4 times.
(9, 18, 27, 36)

What are four 9s?
(36)

Continue to have students count any number 1–10 four times.

Day 4

Pose these questions.

Suppose there are 10 fingers on each of 4 people. How many fingers altogether?
(40 fingers)

Suppose there are 4 sides on each of 4 rectangles. How many sides altogether?
(16 sides)

Continue to present situations with 1–10 items in each of 4 groups, asking

How many altogether?

Day 5

Pose these questions.

Suppose there are 4 scoops of ice cream in each of 2 bowls. How many scoops of ice cream altogether?
(8 scoops of ice cream)

Suppose there are 4 books on each of 6 shelves. How many books altogether?
(24 books)

Continue to present situations with 4 items in each of 1–10 groups, asking

How many altogether?

Four-Row Arrays

●●●

Small Group Activity

Summary

Students partition arrays with four rows into two arrays that are easier to solve. Through this activity, students discover that facts with four as a factor have a product equal to twice the related multiply-by-2 fact.

Materials

One (1) copy of Four-Row Arrays, page 68, for each student

---

reminder Arrays are described as the number of rows times the number of items in each row.

Directions

❶ Work through the first exercise of Four-Row Arrays with your students.

❷ Have students work in pairs to first identify the multiplication fact each four-row array represents and then write that fact in the first set of answer lines after the array.

❸ Pairs should partition each array to make two equal sets of rows. They should then shade one set to show the split. Pairs of students have two copies of the page so that they can try partitioning the array more than one way.

❹ Instruct students to write the multiplication facts that describe the two arrays in the spaces provided. They should complete the sentence by writing the product.

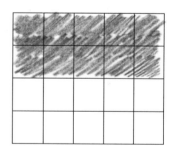

$$4 \times 5 = (2 \times 5) + (2 \times 5) = 20$$

Talk About It

For each array, ask

How did you partition this array? (Answers will vary.)

What facts did you write? (Record the facts on the board. Facts should match student arrays.)

Do you see any patterns that will make it easier to remember your multiply-with-4 facts? (Accept all accurate responses.) The idea that multiplying by 4 is the same as splitting the four into 2×2, multiplying the other factor by 2, and then doubling that product should emerge. If not, organize the facts you have recorded on the board, placing together all the facts of the type $4 \times n = (2 \times n) + (2 \times n)$.

Ask if students see a pattern and how that pattern might make remembering multiplying-with-4 facts easier to recall.

Extension or Homework

Provide a copy of Patterns in a Table, page 69, for each student. After the students have completed the table and answered the questions, have a class discussion to talk about their results. Be sure students notice that the product for a number times 4 is double the corresponding product for the number times 2.

Four-Row Arrays

Separating an array into two parts can help you find a product.

Directions

❶ Write the fact each array represents in the first set of answer lines.

❷ Divide each array into two equal arrays. Shade one of the two arrays.

❸ Write the facts for the new arrays.

❹ Write the product.

1.

_____ × _____ = (_____ × _____) + (_____ × _____) = _____

2.

_____ × _____ = (_____ × _____) + _____ × _____) = _____

3.

_____ × _____ = (_____ × _____) + (_____ × _____) = _____

4.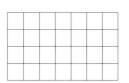

_____ × _____ = (_____ × _____) + (_____ × _____) = _____

5.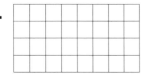

_____ × _____ = (_____ × _____) + (_____ × _____) = _____

Patterns in a Table

What patterns can you discover when you compare the product of a number that has been multiplied by 2 with the product of the same number multiplied by 4?

Directions

1. Complete the table below.

2. On a separate piece of paper, write about the patterns you find when you study the table.

3. Explain how one of those patterns can help you remember the multiplying-4 facts.

	× 2	× 4
0	0	0
1	2	
2		
3		12
4		
5	10	20
6		
7		
8		
9		
10		

Splitting Fours

Practice

Work on these sets of practice exercises until students can get each answer within three (3) seconds. Ask students to tell the whole fact rather than just the answer ("4 × 5 = 20" instead of "20"). When students tell the whole fact, it improves their recall. Try presenting the facts in various ways. Ask the students to listen and reply verbally, or use flash cards and have the students write their facts. Varying the format helps all students focus on the facts.

Talk About It

Ask students to talk about their thinking. Follow up by asking if anyone has a different way to find the answer.

How did you find the answer to the fact?
(Answers will vary.)

If you use the idea that 4 times a number is the same as doubling 2 times that number, how would you figure out 4 × 5?
(Double 2 × 5 = 10 + 10 = 20) Continue with several other multiplication facts that have 4 as a factor.

Day 1

Pose these questions.

What is the double of
2? (4)
2 books? (4 books)
2 flowers? (4 flowers)
2 butterflies? (4 butterflies)
2 quarters? (4 quarters)
2 nines? (4 nines)
2 fives? (4 fives)
2 tens? (4 tens)
2 hundreds? (4 hundreds)
2 fifties? (4 fifties)

Continue to present 2 times a number and have students give you the double.

Day 2

Present these exercises.

What is 2 × 3? (6)

Double your answer to find 4 × 3.
What is 4 × 3? (12)

What is 2 × 8? (16)

Double your answer to find 4 × 8.
What is 4 × 8? (32)

Continue to ask for the product of a multiply-by-2 fact, then have students double the product to find a multiply-by-4 fact.

Day 3

Present these exercises.

4 × 10 is equal to the double of what multiply-by-2 fact? (2 × 10)

4 × 9 is equal to the double of what multiply-by-2 fact? (2 × 9)

4 × 3 is equal to the double of what multiply-by-2 fact? (2 × 3)

4 × 7 is equal to the double of what multiply-by-2 fact? (2 × 7)

Continue to present facts of 4 × any number. Ask students for the multiply-by-2 fact.

Day 4

Present these exercises.

4 × 8 is equal to the double of what multiply-by-2 fact? (2 × 8)

4 × 6 is equal to the double of what multiply-by-2 fact? (2 × 6)

Find these products.

4 × 10 (40)	4 × 3 (12)
2 × 4 (8)	4 × 8 (32)
8 × 4 (32)	7 × 4 (28)
0 × 4 (0)	6 × 4 (24)
4 × 4 (16)	5 × 4 (20)
4 × 7 (28)	9 × 4 (36)
3 × 4 (12)	4 × 4 (16)
10 × 4 (40)	4 × 6 (24)
4 × 1 (4)	4 × 5 (20)

Extension Present facts that have 4 as one factor and the numbers 10–15, in order, as the second factor.

Day 5

Present these facts.

6 × 4 (24)	1 × 4 (4)
4 × 8 (32)	4 × 1 (4)
7 × 4 (28)	3 × 4 (12)
9 × 4 (36)	10 × 4 (40)
5 × 4 (20)	4 × 2 (8)
4 × 4 (16)	4 × 0 (0)
8 × 4 (32)	4 × 3 (12)
4 × 10 (40)	4 × 7 (28)
2 × 4 (8)	4 × 6 (24)
4 × 4 (16)	4 × 5 (20)
0 × 4 (0)	4 × 9 (36)

Extension Present facts that have 4 as one factor and the numbers 10–15, in order, as the second factor.

Ways with Sixes Overview

What are Ways with Sixes?

One method of remembering facts with 6 as a factor involves adding one more group to a multiple of five. For example, 6×7 is 5×7 plus one more 7. Since $5 \times 7 = 35$, when you add one more 7, you get 42.

Another way to remember facts with 6 as a factor is to double multiples of 3. For example, with 6×7, double 3×7, or double 21, to get 42.

When to Use Ways with Sixes

Use ways with sixes for multiplication facts that have six as a factor.

Prerequisites

Students should understand multiplication concepts (pages viii-1). They should know the multiplication facts for multiples of three and five, and they should be able to add a one-digit number to any two-digit number easily.

×	0	1	2	3	4	5	6	7	8	9	10
0							0				
1							6				
2							12				
3							18				
4							24				
5							30				
6	0	6	12	18	24	30	36	42	48	54	60
7							42				
8							48				
9							54				
10							60				

Additional Experiences

Ask students to complete a table like the one shown below. Have students look for patterns that will help them remember the multiplying-6 facts.

You can find additional practice in *Practice Your Facts, Levels 1–5,* by Creative Publications, Inc.

	× 3	× 6	× 5
0			
1			
2			
3			
4			
5			
6			
7			
8			
9			
10			

Ways with Sixes

Warm-ups

Each warm-up exercise set should take two (2) or three (3) minutes. The short sets of exercises are great for filling transition times. Some teachers use them while students stand in line.

Talk About It

As you work through these warm-ups, ask students to talk about their thinking. This not only helps you assess, but gives students a chance to clarify their thinking and to hear about ways of thinking that might be different from theirs. You might ask questions like

What do you notice about multiples of 6?

(Answers might include that they are also multiples of three; they are all even; like the 3s, the sum of the digits can be reduced to 3, 6, or 9. Accept all valid responses.)

A great question to keep the discussion going is

Does anyone have a different answer?

Day 1

Ask students to count as directed.

Count by 6. Start with 6 and count to 60.

(6, 12, 18, 24, 30, 36, 42, 48, 54, 60)

Repeat until most students can count quickly and accurately.

Day 2

Show a number card such as 4.

Count by 6 this many times.

(6, 12, 18, 24)

What are four 6s?

(24)

Show a number card 1–10 to represent the number of times students should count by 6.

Day 3

Show a number card such as 8.

Count by 6 this many times.

(6, 12, 18, 24, 30, 36, 42, 48)

What are eight 6s? (48)

Show a number card 1–10 to represent the number of times students should count by 6.

Day 4

Have students count as directed.

Count by 3. Start with 3 and count 6 times.

(3, 6, 9, 12, 15, 18)

What are six 3s?

(18)

Count by 5. Start with 5 and count 6 times.

(5, 10, 15, 20, 25, 30)

What are six 5s?

(30)

Continue to have students count any number 1–10 six times.

Day 5

Have students count as directed.

Count by 1. Start with 1 and count 6 times.
(1, 2, 3, 4, 5, 6)

What are six 1s?
(6)

Count by 10. Start with 10 and count 6 times.
(10, 20, 30, 40, 50, 60)

What are six 10s?
(60)

Continue to have students count by any number 1–10 six times.

Day 6

Write numbers on the board as indicated.

6 + 6

What multiplication fact and product describes these numbers? (2 × 6 = 12)

6 + 6 + 6 + 6 + 6

What multiplication fact and product describes these numbers? (5 × 6 = 30)

Continue to write 10 or fewer 6s and ask students to describe what you have written with a multiplication fact and product.

Day 7

Pose these questions.

Suppose 6 apples are used in each of 5 pies. How many apples altogether?
(30 apples)

Suppose there are 6 dollars in each of 9 piggy banks. How many dollars altogether?
(54 dollars)

Continue to present situations with 6 items in each of 1–10 groups, asking

How many altogether?

Day 8

Pose these questions.

Suppose there are 6 feathers on each of 7 hats. How many feathers altogether?
(42 feathers)

Suppose there are 6 buttons on each of 4 shirts. How many buttons altogether?
(24 buttons)

Continue to present situations with 6 items in each of 1–10 groups, asking

How many altogether?

Day 9

Pose these questions.

Suppose there are 3 children in each of 6 families. How many children altogether?
(18 children)

Suppose there are 2 parakeets in each of 6 birdcages. How many parakeets altogether?
(12 parakeets)

Continue to present situations with 1–10 items in each of 6 groups, asking

How many altogether?

Day 10

Pose these questions.

Suppose there are 10 leaves on each of 6 branches. How many leaves altogether?
(60 leaves)

Suppose there is 1 birthday candle on each of 6 birthday cakes. How many birthday candles altogether?
(6 birthday candles)

Continue to present situations of 1–10 items in each of 6 groups, asking

How many altogether?

Six-Row Arrays

●●●

Small Group Activity

Summary

As students partition arrays with six rows various ways, two strategies for remembering multiplying-6 facts emerge—doubling multiples of three, and adding another row onto a five row array.

Materials

One (1) copy of Six-Row Arrays, page 80, for each student

Directions

❶ Work through the first exercise of Six-Row Arrays with your students.

❷ Have students work in pairs to first identify the multiplication fact each array of six rows represents and then write that fact in the first set of answer lines after the array.

....

reminder Arrays are described as the number of rows times the number of items in each row.

❸ Instruct students to partition each array into two parts and shade one part to show the split. Each of the new arrays should be an easy multiplication fact (answer can be found quickly and accurately). Pairs of students should have two copies of the page so that they can try partitioning the array more than one way.

❹ Instruct students to write the multiplication facts that describe the two arrays in the spaces provided. They should complete the sentence by writing the product.

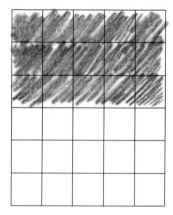

$6 \times 5 = (3 \times 5) + (3 \times 5) = 30$

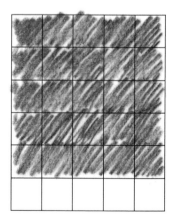

$6 \times 5 = (5 \times 5) + (1 \times 5) = 30$

Talk About It

For each array, ask

How did you partition this array? (Answers will vary.)

What facts did you write? Record the facts on the board.

Do you see any patterns that can make it easier to remember multiplying-by-6 facts? (Accept all correct responses.)

Multiplying by 6 is the same as doubling the product of a related multiplying-by-3 fact. If this idea does not come up in the discussion, organize the facts that you have recorded on the board, placing all the facts of the type $6 \times n = (3 \times n) + (3 \times n)$ together. Then ask if students see a pattern and how that pattern might make remembering multiplying-by-6 facts easier to recall.

Another idea to point out is that multiplying by 6 is the same as multiplying by 5 and adding on one more group. For example, $6 \times n = (5 \times n) + (n)$. If this idea does not emerge from the class discussion, refocus on the partitioning of arrays activity that students completed. Ask students if multiplying by five can help.

Extension Have students look for patterns in the products of the multiplying-6 facts found on Six Patterns, page 81. After they have written about the patterns found, have students share their findings in a class discussion. Observations might include that all multiples of 6 are even, they are also multiples of 3, and the sum of the digits is 3, 6 or 9.

Six-Row Arrays

Separating an array into two parts can help you find a product.

Directions

❶ Write the fact each array represents in the first set of answer lines.

❷ Divide each array into two arrays. Shade one of the two arrays.

❸ Write the facts for the new arrays.

❹ Write the products.

1.

____ × ____ = (____ × ____) + (____ × ____) = ____

2.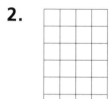

____ × ____ = (____ × ____) + ____ × ____) = ____

3.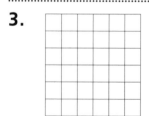

____ × ____ = (____ ×____) + (____ × ____) = ____

4.

____ × ____ = (____ × ____) + (____ × ____) = ____

5.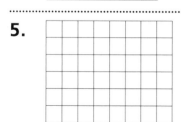

____ × ____ = (____ × ____) + (____ × ____) = ____

Sixes Patterns

Find as many patterns as you can in the products of facts that have six as a factor. These patterns can help you remember your multiplying-6 facts.

$0 \times 6 = 0$

$1 \times 6 = 6$

$2 \times 6 = 12$

$3 \times 6 = 18$

$4 \times 6 = 24$

$5 \times 6 = 30$

$6 \times 6 = 36$

$7 \times 6 = 42$

$8 \times 6 = 48$

$9 \times 6 = 54$

$10 \times 6 = 60$

Directions

1 Look for patterns in these facts.

2 On a separate piece of paper, write about the patterns you find.

3 Explain how one of the patterns you find can help you remember the multiplying-6 facts.

_____

_____

_____

_____

_____

Ways with Sixes

Practice

Work on these sets of practice exercises until students can get each answer within three (3) seconds. Ask students to tell the whole fact rather than just the answer ("3 × 6 = 18," not "18"). When students tell the whole fact, it improves their recall. Try presenting the facts in various ways. Ask the students to listen and reply verbally, or use flash cards and have the students write their facts. Varying the format helps all students focus on the facts.

Talk About It

Ask students to talk about their thinking. Follow up by asking if anyone has a different way to find the answer.

How did you find the answer to that fact?
(Answers will vary.)

If you use the idea that six times a number is equal to doubling three times that number, how do you find 6 × 5?
(Double $3 \times 5 = 15 + 15 = 30$)
Continue with several other multiplication facts that have 6 as a factor.

If you use the idea that six times a number is equal to five times the number plus one more group of the number, how do you find 6 × 7?
(Think $6 \times 7 = 5 \times 7 + 7$. Then $5 \times 7 = 35$, and $35 + 7 = 42$.)
Continue with several other multiplication facts that have 6 as a factor.

....

Day 1

Pose these questions.

What is the double of 3? (6)

What is the double of
3 pencils? (6 pencils)
3 oranges? (6 oranges)
3 children? (6 children)
3 dollars? (6 dollars)
3 hundreds? (6 hundreds)
3 tens? (6 tens)
3 fives? (6 fives)
3 fours? (6 fours)
3 sevens? (6 sevens)

Continue to present 3 items and have students give you the double.

Day 2

Present these exercises.

What is 3 × 5? (15)

Double your answer to find 6 × 5. (30)

What is 3 × 7? (21)

Double your answer to find 6 × 7. (42)

Continue to ask for the product of a multiply-by-3 fact, then have students double the product to find a multiply-by-6 fact.

© Creative Publications 32312

Day 3

Present these exercises.

What is 3 × 8? (24)

Double your answer to find 6 × 8. (28)

What is 3 × 11? (33)

Double your answer to find 6 × 11. (66)

Continue to ask for the product of a multiply-by-3 fact, then have students double the product to find a multiply-by-6 fact.

Day 4

Present these exercises.

6 × 5 is equal to the double of what multiply-by-3 fact? (3 × 5)

6 × 9 is equal to the double of what multiply-by-3 fact? (3 × 9)

6 × 3 is equal to the double of what multiply-by-3 fact? (3 × 3)

6 × 7 is equal to the double of what multiply-by-3 fact? (3 × 7)

Continue to present facts of the type 6 × *n*. Ask students for the multiply-by-3 fact which, when doubled, produces an equal amount.

Day 5

Present these exercises.

6 × 10 is equal to the double of what multiply-by-3 fact? (3 × 10)

6 × 8 is equal to the double of what multiply-by-3 fact? (3 × 8)

6 × 3 is equal to the double of what multiply-by-3 fact? (3 × 3)

6 × 6 is equal to the double of what multiply-by-3 fact? (3 × 6)

Continue to present facts of the type 6 × *n*. Ask students for the multiply-by-3 fact which, when doubled, produces an equal amount.

Day 6

Present these facts.

6 × 7 is equal to the double of what multiply-by-3 fact? (3 × 7)

6 × 12 is equal to the double of what multiply-by-3 fact? (3 × 12)

6 × 10 (60)	3 × 6 (18)
0 × 6 (0)	5 × 6 (30)
6 × 3 (18)	1 × 6 (6)
6 × 9 (54)	4 × 6 (24)
8 × 6 (48)	6 × 4 (24)
9 × 6 (54)	6 × 7 (42)
10 × 6 (60)	0 × 6 (0)
6 × 6 (36)	6 × 1 (6)
7 × 6 (42)	4 × 6 (24)
2 × 6 (12)	6 × 5 (30)
6 × 8 (48)	6 × 6 (36)
6 × 0 (0)	6 × 2 (12)

Extension Present facts that have 6 as one factor and the numbers 11–15, in ascending order, as the second factor.

Day 7

Present these exercises.

What are five 3s? (15)

If we add one more 3 to make six 3s, how much altogether? (18)

What are six 3s? (18)

What are five 7s? (35)

If we add one more 7 to make six 7s, how much altogether? (42)

What are six 7s? (42)

Continue to ask students to give the product of 5 and a number 1–10, then add on one more of the number to make 6 times the number.

Day 8

Present these exercises.

What are five 8s? (40)

If we add one more 8 to make six 8s, how much altogether? (48)

What are six 8s? (48)

What are five 6s? (30)

If we add one more 6 to make six 6s, how much altogether? (36)

What are six 6s? (36)

Continue to ask students to give the product of 5 and a number 1–10, then add on one more of the number to make 6 times the number.

Day 9

Present these facts.

What are five 4s? (20)

If we add one more 4 to make six 4s, how much altogether? (24)

What are six 4s? (24)

What are five 9s? (45)

If we add one more 9 to make six 9s, how much altogether? (54)

What are six 9s? (54)

6 × 10 (60)	3 × 6 (18)
0 × 6 (0)	5 × 6 (30)
6 × 3 (18)	1 × 6 (6)
6 × 9 (54)	4 × 6 (24)
8 × 6 (48)	6 × 4 (24)
9 × 6 (54)	6 × 7 (42)
10 × 6 (60)	0 × 6 (0)
6 × 6 (36)	6 × 1 (6)
7 × 6 (42)	4 × 6 (24)
2 × 6 (12)	6 × 5 (30)
6 × 8 (48)	6 × 6 (36)
6 × 0 (0)	6 × 2 (12)

Extension Present facts that have 6 as one factor and the numbers 11–15, in ascending order, as the second factor.

Day 10

Present these facts.

2 × 6 (12)	4 × 6 (24)
7 × 6 (42)	9 × 6 (54)
6 × 8 (48)	6 × 6 (36)
3 × 6 (18)	1 × 6 (6)
6 × 0 (0)	6 × 4 (24)
5 × 6 (30)	6 × 7 (42)
0 × 6 (0)	0 × 6 (0)
6 × 10 (60)	4 × 6 (24)
6 × 3 (18)	6 × 1 (6)
8 × 6 (48)	6 × 5 (30)
6 × 9 (54)	6 × 2 (12)
10 × 6 (60)	6 × 6 (36)

Extension Present facts that have 6 as one factor and the numbers 11–15, in ascending order, as the second factor.

Multiplication Chart

	0	1	2	3	4	5	6	7	8	9	10
0	0	0	0	0	0	0	0	0	0	0	0
1	0	1	2	3	4	5	6	7	8	9	10
2	0	2	4	6	8	10	12	14	16	18	20
3	0	3	6	9	12	15	18	21	24	27	30
4	0	4	8	12	16	20	24	28	32	36	40
5	0	5	10	15	20	25	30	35	40	45	50
6	0	6	12	18	24	30	36	42	48	54	60
7	0	7	14	21	28	35	42	49	56	63	70
8	0	8	16	24	32	40	48	56	64	72	80
9	0	9	18	27	36	45	54	63	72	81	90
10	0	10	20	30	40	50	60	70	80	90	100

Multiplication Chart

×	0	1	2	3	4	5	6	7	8	9	10
0											
1											
2											
3											
4											
5											
6											
7											
8											
9											
10											

Bibliography

Practice Your Facts. Chicago, Creative Publications, Inc., 1999. These 80-page practice books offer traditional practice on all facts. Levels 1–5.

Brodie, Julie Pier. *Constructing Ideas About Multiplication and Division.* Chicago, Creative Publications, Inc., 1995. Fourteen rich investigations help students develop basic concepts of multiplication and division.

Holden, Linda, and Micaelia Randolph Brummett. *Understanding Multiplication & Division.* Chicago, Creative Publications, Inc., 1988. Forty-eight carefully sequenced, reproducible lessons help students make connections between concrete experiences, pictorial representations, and abstract equations. The 128-page binder includes activities using linking cubes and counting chips.

Irvine, Rhea, and Kathryn Walker. *Smart Arithmetic, Grades 4–6.* Chicago, Creative Publications, Inc., 1995. This 96-page teacher resource book helps you guide your students in a thinking approach to computation as they invent their own algorithms. A start-up bank of suggested activities provides experiences in discourse, visual thinking, mental computation, and fact recall.

National Council of Teachers of Mathematics. *Standards 2000.* Reston, Virginia, 2000. This document emphasizes the importance of mastering basic facts. Indeed, fast and accurate recall of basic facts is an essential tool in the mathematical toolkit.

Pittock, Janet. *Practice Worth Repeating.* Chicago, Creative Publications, Inc., 1999. Help students keep their fact recall fast and accurate with enjoyable practice. These manageable 32-page books include several engaging practice activities that can be used over and over with the same students.

Roper, Ann and Charlene Margot. *Ready to Go! with Base Ten Blocks.* Chicago, Creative Publications, Inc., 1997. This brief overview of base ten blocks summarizes key concepts that can be developed with these useful manipulatives. Tips for classroom management and three classroom-tested activities are included.

Larry Leutzinger, author of the *Facts That Last* series, is an associate professor at the University of Northern Iowa and co-director of the Iowa Mathematics and Science Coalition. Dr. Leutzinger's major interests include teaching mental mathematics concepts, including basic facts, to pre-K through fourth grade students. He is actively researching the knowledge and abilities of those students.